SIZE AND FORM IN PLANTS

MACMILLAN AND CO., Limited
LONDON · BOMBAY · CALCUTTA · MADRAS
MELBOURNE

THE MACMILLAN COMPANY
NEW YORK · BOSTON · CHICAGO
DALLAS · ATLANTA · SAN FRANCISCO

THE MACMILLAN COMPANY
OF CANADA, LIMITED
TORONTO

SIZE AND FORM IN PLANTS

WITH SPECIAL REFERENCE TO THE PRIMARY CONDUCTING TRACTS

BY

F. O. BOWER, Sc.D., LL.D., F.R.S.

EMERITUS PROFESSOR OF BOTANY IN THE
UNIVERSITY OF GLASGOW

WITH 72 FIGURES AND 25 TABLES

MACMILLAN AND CO., LIMITED
ST. MARTIN'S STREET, LONDON
1930

COPYRIGHT

' Rationem verum harum gravitationis proprietarum ex phaenomenis nondum potui deducere, & hypotheses non fingo.'

Newton, *Principia*, 3rd edition, 1726. Reprinted by Messrs. MacLehose, 1871, for Sir William Thomson and Professor Blackburn, p. 530.

PREFACE

In approaching a problem so extended as that of the
relation between Size and Form in Plants at large, it is
desirable in the first instance to select some limited field
of observation : preferably it should be one in which those
difficulties, which increasing size necessarily entails, have
not been so successfully surmounted by adaptation as they
have been in some of the Highest Plants. The features
compared should also be readily open to measurement,
whether the material be in the living or in the fossil state.
The conducting tracts, and in particular the wood which
is as a rule well preserved in fossils, afford the best opportunity for comparative treatment. In the more primitive
Vascular Plants the primary conducting tracts as they
grow larger develop peculiarities of form which have
already aroused curiosity, though this has never been fully
satisfied by theoretical explanation. Their stelar plasticity
appears to present a special opportunity for enquiry
bearing upon the relation of Form to Size : hence the
Pteridophyta have been used here as the chief field of
observation. Nevertheless the discussions contained in
this Volume are by no means restricted to any particular
section of the Vegetable Kingdom, nor yet to the primary
tissues only.

The most comprehensive account of the primary arrangement of the Vascular System, up to 1877, is to be found in
De Bary's *Comparative Anatomy* (Oxford Press, 1884, pp.
232-401). This is, however, a statement of facts rather
than a synthesis, for no theoretical thread traverses the

detailed description, invaluable as that summary itself is. The Stelar Theory of Van Tieghem first opened the way to a synthetic grouping of those facts (1886). But they were treated by him comparatively as objective things, rather than organographically as functional conducting channels. Causality did not enter into his interpretation, which was based upon idealistic views of Form arising from his conception of the Stelar Unit. In this light it was difficult to see any rational explanation of such recurrent features as Polystely or Gamostely in plants phyletically far apart. It was therefore a great step in advance when Jeffrey introduced the conception of the Protostele as the primitive type of stelar unit. But the outlook remained morphological rather than organographic. Thereafter structural data were rapidly accumulated both from living and from fossil types : but still they were regarded as presenting formal rather than functional problems.

Intensive study of the stelar adventures of the Pteridophytes, but particularly of the Leptosporangiate Ferns, has led the author to the views set forth in this Volume. These were first stated in his Presidential Address to the Royal Society of Edinburgh in 1920. The various forms assumed by their conducting tracts were referred back to Galileo's Principle of Similarity, being recognised as consequences of increasing Size. This demanded an increase in the proportion of surface to bulk in tissues which depend for their functional success upon a due maintenance of surfaces of transit. It was perhaps unfortunate that in that Address, as also in some later writings on the same theme, the expression ' limiting factor ' was applied to this effect of increasing Size, in a sense different from that conveyed by Dr. F. F. Blackman, when introducing the term (*Ann. of Bot.*, xix. p. 281). His use of the expression was physiological, and was explained by the following axiom (*l.c.* p. 289) : ' When a process is conditioned as to its rapidity by a number of separate factors, the rate of the process is limited by the pace of the " slowest " factor.' The term ' limiting factor ' having thus been used physiologically and that use explained, it would have been better, I now think, to have held it as being appropriated to such use, and not to have employed the same words also for the organographic conception which is at the back of the present discussion. Here the term ' limiting factor ' is not used. What has been introduced is a conception of much wider morphological significance than that covered by Blackman's axiom. Under the name ' Size-Factor ' is connoted that influence which tends to secure by modification of Form a due levelling up of the proportion of surface to bulk as the Size increases. Whatever that influence may be, the measurements of growing plants that depend on primary development show consistently its effect in modifying Form, external or internal. It may be described as a Morphoplastic Factor. The evidence that it does act in moulding the tissues is widespread, and its incidence is insistent and unavoidable. The development of this conception and a detailed record of the results of its action form the substance of this book.

An attempt has thus been made to extend to internal tissue-masses the Organographic Method introduced by Von Sachs in his classical Lectures on the ' Physiology of Plants,' and developed by Von Goebel in his *Organographie*, chiefly in relation to external form. The result has been to show that certain of the characteristic mouldings which the inner tracts assume arise independently of the insertion, or even of the existence of appendages ; however deeply those tracts may be thus modified where appendages are present, and particularly where they are large.

Hitherto it has not been found possible to assign an immediate cause to this moulding effect, though it brings important consequences, whether physiological or mor-

phological. Hence the expression ' Size-Factor ' has been
used without defining it except by its results : although
its action may be located in near relation to the apical cone,
or in the embryo itself. The attitude thus adopted towards
an undoubted factor is justified by the broad logic of
Science, and by the practice of its highest votaries. Dam-
pier-Whetham, speaking of the Theory of Gravitation,
notes that when Newton put together his great physical
synthesis, he himself pointed out that the cause of gravita-
tional force remained unknown (*History of Science*, Introduction, p. xv). Newton's own words in the *Principia*
may be translated thus : ' Hitherto I have not been able
to discover the cause of these properties of gravity from
phaenomena, and I frame no hypotheses.' Likewise in its
own more restricted field of botanical phenomena, the
Size-Factor may be recognised as effective in development,
though the immediate cause of its effectiveness is still
unknown.

There has been in late years a tendency to segregate
botanical specialists into two camps : the physiologists
who study function, and the morphologists who study form.
Either side is liable through imperfect knowledge of the
work of the other to adopt mistaken opinions. The best
corrective to this will be not only to table the facts on
either side, but also, as in this book, to make a conscious
attempt to occupy the middle ground. Here certain
structural facts have been stated in their relation to
function: in fact they have been treated organographically.
For this purpose a very considerable field of observation
has been advanced, with approximate rather than absolute
measurements. Certain conclusions as to Size and Form
have followed, and they are set down here in their biological
aspect. It is the hope of the author that by venturing thus
upon a comprehensive statement of fact and inference from
the side of Morphology, the problems of the physiologist

may present themselves with an added interest and point, and that the result may be a better common understanding.

In the preparation of this book much assistance has been received from the Botanical Department of Glasgow University. Not only has Professor Drummond made valuable criticisms and suggestions, but other members of the Staff, and particularly Dr. Williams, have discussed relative matters with me : while liberal use has been made of the calculations and drawings of Dr. Wardlaw, published in the *Transactions of the Royal Society of Edinburgh*. To all of these grateful acknowledgement is here made. I wish also to record my gratitude to Professor W. H. Lang, for valuable advice and help.

F. O. BOWER.

RIPON, *May*, 1930.

CONTENTS

INTRODUCTORY NOTE

THE Size-Relation in Plants has already been the subject of discussion in an Essay by Sachs (*Flora*, vol. lxxvii, 1893, pp. 49-81). His treatment was speculative rather than observational, and dealt with cellular construction rather than with the more general size-relations of tissues or parts. He raised the question why a given plant has its customary dimensions, and cannot appear as a magnified or reduced image of the original, fifty times or one fiftieth of its normal size. He points out how this would be mechanically and physiologically impossible. He suggests the existence of a Correlation between Size and Organisation : and how in the advancing constitution of the organism Nature probably made many failures, but settled down to types dictated under the influence of that inner correlation. He illustrates this by discussion of cell-size rather than of form of tissue-masses. It is this latter mode of illustration that is supplied by the measurements detailed in this Volume : and the present discussion has been based upon a wide range of actual observation of the Form of parts, and of their tissue-masses.

CHAPTER I

STATEMENT OF THE PROBLEM OF SIZE

GROWTH is a general feature of Organic Life. It is exhibited in more or less degree in the development of each individual organism, and the varying contours of the adult may be held as illustrating in each the balance between the impulse to growth, and those modifying conditions under which it has been carried out. There is a prevalent difference between the Animal Kingdom and the Kingdom of Plants in the way in which the adult state is reached. In both the individual springs normally from a single cell, and in all the higher forms a juvenile stage precedes the adult. In the Higher Animals this embryological period is limited : the initiation of members in relation to the central trunk is definite as regards their number, and after the first stages are past there is no further initiation of such parts. In them embryogeny is a phase that is passed through and definitely closed, so far as the initiation of new parts is concerned ; the adult size being attained by growth of the parts themselves established early. But in Plants, excepting the simplest of them, there is a continued embryogeny, which is not closed except under stress of circumstances. The formation of members or appendages is not carried out once for all, as in Animals : but in all the higher forms of plant-life a succession of parts may be produced. In fact the embryogeny of the Higher Plants is continued on a scheme theoretically without term or limit.

Herbert Spencer has contrasted this scheme of construction of the plant-body physiologically with that seen in animals. He pointed out how the latter are limited in their development by the balance of expenditure against nutrition : for during life they undergo a waste which increases with the dimensions on a higher scale than does their assimilation. Plants on the other hand are accumulators : they are in no appreciable degree expenders. Accordingly there is in plants no reason why their growth should be arrested by the equilibration of assimilation and waste (*Principles of Biology*, vol. ii, p. 125). Naturally development under circumstances not so controlled may be expected to lead to problems of size, cognate it is true with those in animals, but different in degree and in detail. Such problems in living things may be regarded either as mechanical or morphoplastic. The former aspect would apply equally to both animals and plants, just as it would to unorganised structures, such as bridges or buildings. But the morphoplastic problems, though also cognate for both kingdoms, may be expected to work out differently since the one kingdom comprises organisms of high expenditure, while those of the other are essentially accumulators.

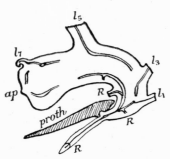

Fig. 1.—*Polypodium vulgare.* (× 6.) Median section through a prothallus (shaded) and embryo (clear), partly diagrammatic. l_1-l_7, one series only of the distichous leaves. R = roots, ap = growing point of stem. The axis is small where it is attached to the prothallus, but it increases obconically upwards.

A natural consequence of this in plants is that, starting from relatively small beginnings, those of primitive type, and endowed with continued apical growth, may commonly be seen to increase distally in the size and number of their parts. The sporeling of a Fern bears a succession of leaves, each normally larger than its predecessor : and these are borne upon an axis of obconical form, the cusp or tip of the cone being the organic base while there is a gradual expansion upwards (Fig. 1). The same holds in more or less degree for all primary types of land-vegetation. Its effect may be seen with special clearness at the base of a *Pandanus* or of Maize. The result is a body of inherently unstable equilibrium, which would become mechanically impossible as growth proceeds, were it not for accessory aids. These appear as the strut-roots commonly seen in Ferns, and still more prominently in a *Pandanus* or a Palm. But the mechanical difficulty is much more efficiently met by secondary growth, which results from cambial activity. This has been initiated in many Peridophytes, but it is worked out to a state of high success in the trunks of ordinary forest trees. The obconical form would also become increasingly difficult physiologically, were it not for such adjustments as result from cambial activity. Nevertheless many primitive vascular plants have been able, without cambial increase, to meet the physiological demands of a shoot that enlarges upwards : for they show distally a progressive adjustment of the primary internal structure. That this proves sufficient for their needs is witnessed by the survival of such plants as Ferns, Lycopods, and Psilotaceae. Such plants provide material of greater value in the study of the size-factor than do those more successful types which possess secondary thickening. It is then through the study of the relatively primitive vascular plants that the problem of size may best be approached. Examples of their methods of adjustment of tissues, and of the relation of their structure to increasing size will be given in the earlier chapters of this book : while those which possess secondary thickening will be held over for later treatment.

The Principle of Similarity, first enunciated by Galileo, reigns supreme over all structures, whether unorganised as in buildings and the engineering works of man, or organised as in animals or plants. Its mechanical application affects stability and strength : its physiological application in the living organism works out through the proportion of any limiting surface to the bulk of the tissues enclosed by it. It may be proved mathematically that as the size increases the strength of a structure increases as the square of the linear dimensions, but the weight or mass as the cube, provided the form and material remain the same : also that in similar solid figures whatever their form, provided that on enlargement the same form be maintained, the surface increases as the square, and the bulk or volume as the cube of the linear dimensions.

From the time of Stephen Hales this principle has been widely illustrated in its application to the bodies of animals, and many of their peculiarities of form and structure have been recognised as necessary consequences of its effect in the course of their evolution. As a mechanical instance, the columnar legs of the Elephant or of the Moa are held to be the inevitable sequel to the large size and consequent weight of those mobile animals : while the thin arched legs of insects are only possible where the body itself is small and light. Such questions have been adequately dealt with in D'Arcy Thompson's book on *Growth and Form* (Cambridge, 1917), where the literature up to the date of its publication is fully quoted. Botanists have, however, been slower in applying the Principle of Similarity to the study of plants. It is true that the question of the practicable limit of the height of trees has long ago been discussed from this point of view, and it has been recognised that a change, either of material or of the method of construction, would be necessary for effective growth beyond the limits already reached by some of the largest of them. In fact that 300 feet or rather more is the extreme height that can be self-supporting with the usual construction of the woody trunk : and that is the approximate level of the highest canopy in tropical forests. Naturally the mechanical limit does not actually control the earliest stages of growth of the individual, though mechanical requirements will need to be met all through the ontogenetic history.

These will influence the shape and proportions of the growing trunk and branches, and so may have a continuous morphoplastic effect. But they will only impose a final limit when an undue proportion of weight and strain to strength has been reached (see D'Arcy Thompson, *l.c.* p. 19 ; also Greenhill, *Camb. Phil. Soc. Proc.* iv, 1881, p. 65, etc.).

The incidence of a mechanical limit is, however, only one way in which the Principle of Similarity applies to living organisms. A much more intimate and far-reaching influence of the size-factor on their construction arises from progressive change in the proportion of surface to bulk in growing cells, tissues, or parts. The importance of this lies in the fact that physiological interchange, which is inseparable from active life, is conducted through limiting surfaces, external or internal. It may be assumed that, other things being equal, and where the surface is continuous and unbroken, such interchange will be directly proportional to the area of surface involved. But if the form be maintained unchanged in a growing cell, tissue, or part, according to the Principle of Similarity while the bulk increases as the cube of the linear dimensions, the surface increases only as the square. Consequently there would be a constantly decreasing proportion of surface to bulk, and as constantly an approach to a point of physiological inefficiency. This result would follow in any growing individual, whether animal or plant ; and equally in any enlarging race of individuals, provided the original form of cell, tissue, or part be maintained unaltered. On the other hand, any change from a simple form, such as a sphere or cylinder or cone, which gives a more complicated contour will increase the proportion of surface to bulk ; for instance, corrugation or fluting of the surface, or branching and segregation into parts : and the same applies also for bodies of more elaborate form than those named. Thus increasing morphological complexity involving any increased complication of form would tend to meet the physiological need consequent on increasing size, by tending to level up the proportion of surface to bulk.

In the construction of any ordinary Vascular Plant there are three limiting tissue-surfaces of prime importance : (i) the outer contour of the plant or part, complicated though it usually is in sub-aerial plants by the added cell-surfaces lining the ventilating channels ; (ii) the endo-dermal sheath, which delimits the conducting tracts from the tissues that envelop them ; and (iii) the collective surface by which the dead tracheal system faces upon the living cells or tissues that embed it. Each of these is a surface of physiological transit, and each independently of the others will be a suitable subject for observation from the point of view of the proportion of surface to bulk as the size increases.

In order to obtain a clear outlook on such a question as this, it should be approached from an evolutionary point of view, and be studied first in those plants that are of more ancient type and of simpler organisation, rather than in the most elaborate and recent. For instance, the solid tra-cheidal core of a primitive protostele presents a simpler problem than the woody column of a complex tree-trunk, which is intimately permeated by parenchyma : or again, the simple surface of a plant or part without stomata as compared with a part bearing stomata. In fact the study of the size-factor should be regarded not only as a problem of physiological anatomy, but also as one of evolutionary progress under varying conditions. The more simple and primitive the structure the more clearly may the size-factor be isolated from such complications, mostly of later evolutionary origin, which tend to confuse the issue. Accordingly the following discussion will be concentrated on primitive rather than on the highest derivative types.

Herein lies a probable reason why this study has not received the attention it deserves in the comparative morphology and physiology of the tissues of plants, and particularly in that of the vascular system. As in so many like questions the more advanced types of construction seen in Seed-Plants, were the first to be examined : this the history of the science plainly shows. The tissues of these, or even their whole parts have habitually been used as basal types, in the light of which the lower forms were to be interpreted ; instead of the higher forms being themselves regarded as derivative, and subject to interpretation in terms of the lower. This was realised long ago in regard to external form, but at the present day the reverse applies very generally to the study of internal structure. For instance it is often forgotten in the discussion of sub-aerial parts that internal ventilation, with stomata and lenticels as outlets, is a derivative state. But as a matter of fact the Thallophytes, as well as the whole Gametophyte generation, have been evolved without them. From an evolutionary point of view internal ventilation itself should be regarded as a relatively late concession to the requirement of a due proportion of surface to bulk (under stomatal control) in enlarging sub-aerial parts, rather than as a primary starting point in physiology. The study of the Bryophytes from this point of view reveals the shifts to which sub-aerial organisms having no internal ventilation have been driven, so as to level up the deficiency in proportion of surface to bulk as they increase in size.

On the other hand, the disintegrated conducting tracts of the higher vascular plants, and particularly their secondary tissues, are habitually used as a basis for the study of the channels of transit. Here the woody elements are throughout permeated by living parenchyma, and are even provided with a ventilating system of intercellular spaces through the medullary rays. The physiological difficulties of increasing size have thus been effectively met, and so do not fasten the attention of the student. Yet the vascular tissues of the higher plants are presented first to the beginner in ordinary text-books. The fact is apt to be forgotten or ignored that the conducting tracts of the most primitive vascular plants had a solid woody core, consisting of a mass of tracheids without any parenchyma included in it, and wholly unventilated. To obtain a logical sequence the whole presentment would need to be inverted : the complex conducting tracts of seed-plants should be approached through the study of the primitive types, if a proper understanding of their structural evolution and advancing efficiency is to be gained. More particularly is this desirable when the conducting system is considered in its relation to the factor of size.

Partly then to secure a logical sequence of observation, partly in order to approach the study of size in its true morphogenic bearing, the higher and more complex types of construction will be left provisionally on one side. Evidence will in the first instance be drawn from the simplest examples of the vascular system ; and as far as possible actual measurements will be considered, rather than mere pictorial representation. Relatively primitive plants, such as the early Pteridophytes, will be described first, particularly those in which secondary thickening is either absent, or appears only as a late incident in development. In these special attention will be given to the collective surface of exposure between tracheids and living cells. For the maintenance of the large and diffuse living body of the plant a large surface of interchange is required between the living body and the dead elements of the wood, which modern physiology regards collectively as a reservoir of liquid food-stuffs within the plant (see H. H. Dixon, *The Transpiration Stream,* London, 1924, p. 73).

In drawing this introductory statement to a close, another circumstance may be mentioned which has certainly tended to obscure the proper realisation of the incidence of the size-factor in plant-morphology. It is the haphazard use of scale in the presentment of results. In the earlier developmental work it was a common thing for no exact scale of magnification of the drawings to be given at all. Even where the magnification is stated accurately the scale is often adjusted arbitrarily, according to convenience in placing the figures on the page or plate. It is

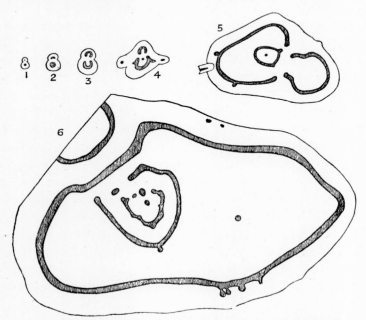

FIG. 2.—Series of transverse sections of the stem of *Pteris* (*Litobrochia*) *podophylla*, all drawn to the same scale, so as to show the great increase in size, and the progressive complexity of the conducting tracts (shaded) as the stem expands conically upwards. (× 4.)

a comparatively rare thing to find developmental descriptions accompanied by illustrative sequences all drawn to the same scale. The eye is misled by the inconstancy of scale, and the imagination of the reader has difficulty in realising how greatly the objects represented have increased in size as the development proceeds (Fig. 2).

As is intimated by the sub-title, the present work will relate mainly to the conducting tracts of relatively primitive plants, though other tissues and higher organisms will also be considered. The facts of change of form that accompany ontogenetic increase in size will be presented in orderly sequence, and as far as possible upon the same scale, in a number of plants held as primitive. From these it will be possible to extend comparison to those which are more advanced, and to trace in them such adjustments of form and structure as have contributed to their evolutionary success. It must not, however, be expected that a consistent numerical proportion must always appear. The size-factor is only one among many which may influence form. Moreover many organisms show a strange conservatism of archaic characters, holding on to them in spite of the seeming disadvantages entailed. In particular, a number of ancient types, such as the fossil Osmundaceæ, the Sphenophylls, and many Lepidodendraceæ, retained their large tracts of purely tracheidal wood ; and the like may still be seen in some Ferns, such as the living Osmundaceæ. The elimination of plants showing such structure may be held rather as evidence of its unsuitability, than as disproof of the importance of the size-factor in the evolution of the conducting system in living plants of like affinity. It is, indeed, a significant fact that no really large plant, without cambial increase, lives to-day in which the primary wood consists of tracheal elements only.

In later pages the influence of the size-factor on form will be traced along broader lines than these, and analogies will be traced over a more extended field. Thus it may be shown that the principle of similarity is of wide application in relation to form and structure. But yet it must always be borne in mind that the actual contour of cells, tissues, or plant-parts is to be held as the resultant of the interaction of all those factors which influence their development.

It has been pointed out that in the construction of any ordinary vascular plant there are three limiting tissue-surfaces, that call for special attention in relation to the size-factor : viz. (i) the superficial contour, (ii) the endodermal sheath, and (iii) the collective surface by which the dead tracheal system faces the living tissues that surround or permeate it. Each of these limiting surfaces may react independently of the others as the size increases. Nevertheless they may react simultaneously, and along parallel lines if the circumstances demand it. Those which are most closely related are the two last named. Consequently in many plants these two surfaces may show a like outline when seen in transverse section, as they habitually do in any Fern stem. But they may also react differently, with the result that they do not follow a parallel course in the transverse section. It will be seen that the limiting surface between dead wood and living parenchyma is much more delicately susceptible to the demand of a due proportion of surface to bulk than is the endodermal layer. Consequently while the latter may preserve a circular or oval contour in transverse section as the parts enlarge, the former may show irregularly sculptured surfaces. That will be demonstrated in the Psilotaceæ and Lycopods, while it is a constant feature in roots of moderate size. On the other hand, the superficial contour of the whole organ, which faces the external medium in which it grows, is much less susceptible : particularly is this so where the surface is perforated by stomata leading to the internal ventilating channels. Consequently this surface habitually maintains a smooth contour, even where the conducting system within is broken up into an elaborate meshwork of meristeles, as it is in many stems or leaves. These statements will severally receive support from the facts to be detailed in the following chapters, and reasons for divergence of behaviour may be suggested when the facts have been described. Meanwhile it must not be assumed, from this divergence, that the incidence of the size-factor is negligible as the size increases. It would be more in accord with a scientific outlook to seek a separate explanation for each divergence of behaviour : realising meanwhile that the growing plant, as a whole as well as in its parts, is throughout its development subject to the principle of similarity, as are all other structures organised or unorganised.

The general problem of size in relation to the Morphology of Plants may then be briefly stated thus. Some simple initial form such as is seen in the bodies of primitive plants suffices for small organisms. It is also seen in the embryonic state of all larger types. Plants are, however, accumulators of material rather than expenders, and are theoretically capable of unlimited growth. If that growth were to result in mere enlargement, so that the adult is nothing more than the magnified image of the juvenile state, the organism as it grew would become progressively inefficient, whether mechanically or physiologically. The original scheme of construction requires to be constantly amended, in accordance with the principle of similarity, by changes of plan, or by other adjustments, to meet those demands that follow from increasing size. The ways in which changes or adjustments of form are made in the enlarging organism give an important field for morphological enquiry: especially is this so where change is related to physiological needs. The subject might suitably be styled ' Morphoplasy, or the study of the plasticity of form.' After the more elementary changes in relation to size have been examined in relatively simple examples, more advanced types may be compared with them, and the secondary changes which they adopt be elucidated from a similar point of view. Thus the problem of size as it affects advancing vegetation would be studied in a logical sequence.

CHAPTER II

PSILOTALES AND PSILOPHYTALES, ETC.

SINCE the Memoirs of Kidston and Lang on the Fossils of
the Rhynie Chert were published, the Psilotales have been
confirmed in their position as relatively primitive land
plants. This follows not only from the occurrence of the
Psilophytales in the early Devonian rocks, but also from
the simple morphology of both. They provide, whether in
the fossils or in the living types, material suitable for the
study of primitive structure in relation to increasing size.
The basal region whether of *Psilotum* or of *Tmesipteris* is
leafless and rootless : either genus would serve as a test of
the relation of structure to size, for they both enlarge
conically upwards. The conducting strand with its delimiting endodermis and its central tracheidal strand also
enlarges : the woody core may start from a single tracheid
as seen in transverse section of the embryo of *Tmesipteris*,
and it expands upwards with such changes of structure
and outline as suggest a relation to increasing size
(Holloway, *Trans. N.Z. Inst.* vol. 1, 1918, Figs. 79-83).

The observations and drawings to be first discussed in
detail here were made upon successive sections prepared
by Dr. Wardlaw from a single rhizome of *Psilotum*. He
followed the enlarging structure upwards into the base of
the stout aerial stem, the whole tract being independent
of branching, or of any vascular disturbance by the insertion of appendages (Fig. 3, 1-11). The inner limit of the
endodermis is dotted in his drawings, and this serves to
indicate the dimensional changes of the stele. A simple
solid xylem-core is seen at the base of the series : but as

13

the size increases its outline in transverse section soon becomes more elaborate, giving the suggestion of an encroachment of individual parenchymatous cells into the mass (1-3) : these where they meet will naturally appear

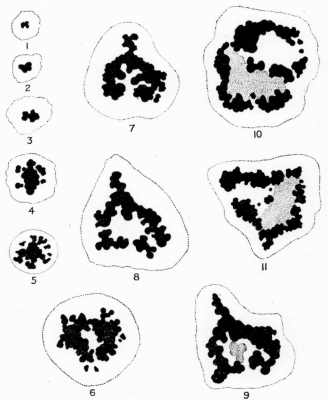

FIG. 3.—*Psilotum triquetrum*, Sw. Series of sections drawn all to the same scale (× 46), from the base of the rhizome, passing into the stout aerial stem, of the same plant. They represent the stele only. Xylem black : sclerotic tissue stippled : endodermis as a dotted line. See Text.

to detach single tracheids or small groups of them from the rest (4). Still higher up the central core becomes progressively disintegrated (5) : further increase in size leads to the constitution of a parenchymatous pith, with further disintegration of the xylem (6-8) ; but part of the pith becomes irregularly sclerosed later (9-11). The largest sections are clearly the most highly disintegrated. Early steps in that disintegration are shown in detail in Wardlaw's figure 2 (*Trans. R.S. Edin.* vol. liii, 1924, p. 511).

Such results as these raise the question of the approximate change in proportion of the collective surface to the bulk of the tracheidal tract itself, exclusive of the living cells that embed it : for what we must study specially is not the so-called ' xylem ' as a whole, but that collective surface by which the dead tracheids abut upon living tissue. We must follow the actual changes in its proportion to the collective bulk of the tracheids as the size increases : for it is this *surface of presentation* which is really important in relating the specialised reservoir of liquid food-stuffs constituted by the tracheids to the tissues it supplies (H. H. Dixon, *The Transpiration Stream*, London, 1924, p. 73). The necessary measurements and calculations have been made by Dr. Wardlaw, based upon the drawings shown in Fig. 3. The results are given in Table I (p. 16), columns III and IV.

From column III it is apparent that the ratio of surface to bulk progressively decreases as the size increases notwithstanding that, as described verbally in column V, the form of its transverse section becomes more complex. The actual decrease in ratio is found to be *to about one third*. But against this must be placed the results shown in column IV, in which are given the like ratios for successive sections, supposing the form of the xylem as a whole to have been throughout that of a simple cylinder, instead of being increasingly complicated in outline as it actually is. If it had retained the cylindrical form the ratio of surface to bulk would have decreased in a much higher ratio than it actually does in the specimen analysed. The figures in column IV show a proportional diminution *to approximately one seventh*. The conclusion follows that the actual decrease in ratio, on passing from the small and simple stele below to the larger and disintegrated stele above, as seen in Fig. 3, is such as will tend to maintain a higher proportion of surface to bulk than would have been the case supposing the enlarging tract of xylem to have retained a cylindrical, or approximately cylindrical form (compare figures in columns III, IV, for sections shown in Fig. 3). Nevertheless that ratio for the largest section seen in Fig. 3 is not so high as it was in the smallest section : the further conclusion then follows that, assuming the maintenance of a high ratio to be of functional importance, *there is an advantage in the increasing complication of form over any mere magnification of the original image : but that advantage does not wholly suffice to preserve the original ratio.*

TABLE I

I Number of Section.	II Diameter of Stele in mm.	III Ratio of Bulk to Surface.	IV Ratio of Bulk to Surface in Equivalent Cylinder.	V REMARKS.
1	·17	1 : 9·26	1 : 6·82	Protostele, xylem solid.
2	·18	1 : 7·31	1 : 4·91	Protostele, xylem solid.
3	·24	1 : 5·90	1 : 4·15	Xylem solid.
4	·29	1 : 5·40	1 : 1·88	Xylem solid, slightly fluted.
5	·26	1 : 5·23	1 : 1·70	Xylem irregularly stellate.
6	·53	1 : 3·64	1 : 1·08	Xylem irregularly stellate, excentric pith beginning.
7	·56	1 : 3·12	1 : 0·97	Irregular excentric pith.
8	·61	1 : 3·20	1 : 0·91	Xylem triangular, pith stellate.
9	·64	1 : 3·12	1 : 0·87	Irregular pith, partly sclerosed
10	·75	1 : 3·00	1 : 0·81	Xylem interrupted cylinder, pith sclerosed.
11	·64	1 : 3·15	1 : 0·95	Xylem interrupted cylinder, pith sclerosed.

For Wardlaw's calculation of proportion of bulk to surface in an equivalent cylinder as stated in column IV, see the original Memoir, *Trans. R.S.E.* vol. liii, p. 510. In columns III, IV, the bulk is stated as unity.

It is worthy of note that the structure of the xylem in the underground parts of *Psilotum* may often be more distinctly stellate in section than is shown in Dr. Wardlaw's drawings. C. E. Bertrand in his exhaustive memoir on the genus presents a transverse section from a very large underground stock where seven rays are present, and the xylem-tracts (mostly distinct, for the leafless stock was young) surround a thin-walled central tissue. This shows that the radial or fluted structure may originate without

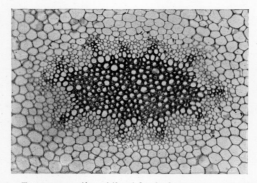

FIG. 4.—Transverse section of the stele of a large and apparently leafless stem of *Psilotum*, showing ten distinct xylic rays : the central tissue is sclerotic. After a photograph by Gwynne-Vaughan.

any influence of appendages, and it clearly leads to an enhanced proportion of surface to bulk (*Arch. Bot. du Nord*, Lille, 1881, p. 373, Fig. 162). In a large and apparently leafless stem of *Psilotum* the xylic tract of which gave a mean diameter of ·6 mm., Gwynne-Vaughan found ten distinct rays, one of them being slightly forked (Fig. 4). The question then arises of the relation of the number of rays or flanges to the size of the xylic tract, in examples where such radial structure is seen. This may be illustrated by comparison of a series of sections taken by C. E. Bertrand from subterranean rhizomes of *Psilotum*, which bear no appendages (*l.c.* Figs. 130-162). The dimensions of a selection of them, with two to seven flanges are embodied in the subjoined table. The measurements were

taken from the sections as figured, and it is assumed that
the scale was the same for them all, though this is not
specifically stated by the author.

TABLE II

Number of Figure.	Diameter of Stele as Figured in mm.	Rays.	Ratio of Diameter to Number of Rays.
130	20	2	10·0
151	32	3	10·3
175	40	4	10·0
161	60	5	12·0
162	70	7	10·0

A special interest here lies in the high degree of constancy
of the ratio of number of the flanges to the diameter. It
will be noted that the ratio for Fig. 161 is divergent : it
was inserted to show that the constancy is not perfect.
Similar measurements have been made from Gwynne-
Vaughan's slides 407, 409, 411, with like results. Hence we
conclude that such elaboration of surface as may follow
from stellation in *Psilotum* progresses with a high degree
of uniformity as the size increases : this tends to maintain
the proportion of surface to bulk of the tracheidal tracts.
The effect of it is similar in nature to the less regular disintegration of the xylem illustrated by Wardlaw. The
changes are not really dissimilar, and either may be held as
a set off to the contingent loss of presentation surface
consequent on increasing size.

Dr. Wardlaw has carried out similar observations on the
basal region of the shoot in *Tmesipteris*, with like results
(*l.c.* p. 512). Comparison may next be made with related
fossils.

PSILOPHYTALES, ETC.

The fossils discovered at Rhynie vary in their dimensions.
The smallest is *Rhynia Gwynne-Vaughani* : *Hornea Lignieri*

may be taken as a middle type : while the largest is *Asteroxylon Mackiei*. A still larger species, *A. elberfeldense*, has been described from the Middle Devonian of North-West Germany by Kräusel and Weyland. Thus the materials are at hand for comparison in respect of the size and structure of their vascular tracts : for the conducting tissues are roughly co-ordinate in size with that of the plants they serve.

In the smallest of these fossils the vascular system consisted of a simple cylindrical stele composed of a slender solid strand of tracheids with broad annular rings, and

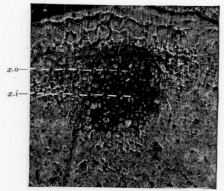

FIG. 5.—*Hornea Lignieri*, stele of stem in transverse section. The solid core of wood is differentiated into outer and inner regions (*x.o—x.i*). (× 60.) From Scott's *Studies*. After Kidston and Lang. (II, VII, Fig. 47.)

there was no distinction of protoxylem and metaxylem. Surrounding the wood was a zone of phloem consisting of elongated and thin-walled elements. In *Rhynia Gwynne-Vaughani* the greater diameter of the slightly oval xylem was ·156 mm. (Kidston and Lang, *Memoir I*, Pl. VII, Fig. 45). A similar dimension is found in the smaller twigs of other and larger plants, and in them a like simplicity of structure is seen. In *Hornea Lignieri* the diameter of the xylem may sometimes be larger : for instance the xylem core may be ·3 mm. in diameter (*l.c. Memoir II*, Pl. VII, Fig. 51) : but the column is still solid and of cylindrical form (Fig. 5). *Asteroxylon* was, however, a much larger plant.

In its rhizome and its smaller twigs the stele may still resemble those of *Rhynia* and *Hornea* : but the larger upright trunks attained a much greater diameter of the stele. The transition from the simpler state of the rhizome to the more complex stele of the leafy shoot appears to find a parallel in that already seen in the Psilotaceæ. As in them it is associated with the appearance of small scale-leaves : but here the stele is relatively large : for instance

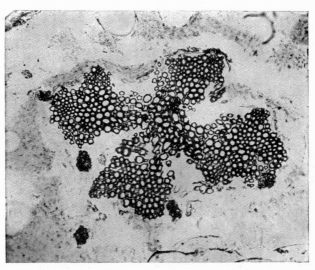

FIG. 6.—*Asteroxylon Mackiei.* Transverse section of the stellate xylem, of a large stem, with leaf-traces departing from the enlarged ends of the rays, but without any regularity of insertion upon them. From Scott's *Studies.* After Kidston and Lang (III, Pl. VII, Fig. 55). (× 33.)

in a stele of *A. Mackiei* the woody column measured over 2·0 mm. in its greater diameter, with a mean diameter of 1·8 mm. (Fig. 6). Its outline is strongly stellate, with four major rays, a structure comparable on the one hand with the xylem of *Psilotum,* and on the other with that seen in the *Selago* type of *Lycopodium.* The outline of the xylem-star as a whole is circular or oval, while the ends of its rays are enlarged, giving the appearance as though plates of the softer phloem had intruded upon an otherwise cylindrical tract of wood. The number of rays of the star is here four, but larger numbers may be found in other examples, especially where a branch is about to be given off. Small leaf-traces spring from the enlarged arms of the xylem, but their relation to these as regards position is not exact or regular : a fact which supports the view that the stellate condition results from extension of the phloem into an otherwise cylindrical column, and does not depend upon the position of the appendages.

Kräusel and Weyland have described as *A. elberfeldense* a still larger species, in which the major diameter of the woody core is 2·8 mm., and the mean about 2·2 mm. This larger size is accompanied by a still greater elaboration of surface so that ten major rays are seen in the stellate section, while the centre was occupied by a considerable area of pith. Another fossil, *Schizopodium*, recently described by Mr. T. Harris from the Devonian Rocks of Australia (*Phil. Trans. B.* vol. ccxvii, p. 395), may be mentioned here as presenting a stellate stele. It is provisionally referred by him to the Asteroxylaceæ, though it possesses a peculiar form of cambial activity. Leafless stems of progressive sizes show advancing steps of stellation, though not with constant relation to the actual measurement. Taking Mr. Harris's restoration of an axis about 5 mm. in diameter as a basis for comparison (*l.c.* Fig. 1), the deeply grooved xylem-star having a diameter of about 2·25 mm. presents 13 rays as defined by their protoxylems, but only 7 as marked by deep involutions.

For comparison as regards the relation of structure of the woody tract to size, the stem of *Cladoxylon scoparium* may also be introduced here. It has been examined by Kräusel and Weyland (*Beitr. z. K. der Devonflora*, ii, 1926, pp. 144-6). Their figures, 39-44, were taken serially, at distances of 5 mm. apart, from a single stem that tapered upwards. The structure shows progressive simplification according to diminishing size. The lowest here quoted (Fig. 44) had 25 rays, with a diameter of 3·7 mm., a middle section (Fig. 42) had 16 rays with a diameter of 2·8 mm., but an upper section (Fig. 40) had only 10 with a diameter of 2·25 mm. These figures are included in Table III in basipetal order, so as to bring out the relation of the number of rays to size, for purposes of comparison with the measurements of the Psilophytales. Though the systematic position of *Cladoxylon* may not be in near alliance to that Class, the facts indicate that a similar size-relation to the structure of the conducting tracts applies for both.

The data for the Psilophytales, and those for *Schizopodium* and *Cladoxylon* may now be tabulated thus:

TABLE III

Name.	Source.	Diameter of Xylem in mm.	REMARKS.
Rhynia Gwynne-Vaughani -	Kidston and Lang I, Pl. VII, Fig. 45.	·156	Roughly cylindrical.
Hornea Lignieri -	II, Pl. VII, Fig. 51.	·3	Roughly cylindrical.
Asteroxylon Mackiei - -	III, Pl. VII, Fig. 55.	1·8	Stellate : 4 major rays.
A. Elberfeldense -	Kräusel and Weyland Text Fig. 8, p. 122.	2·2	Stellate and medullated : 10 major rays.
Schizopodium Davidi - -	Harris, *Phil. Trans.* vol. ccxvii, p. 397, Fig. 1.	2·25	13 protoxylem-groups : 7 actual rays.
Cladoxylon scoparium -	Kräusel and Weyland, *Abh. Senck. Nat. Ges.* Bd. 40.		The order of succession of sections is basipetal See Text.
,,	Fig. 40.	2·25	10 rays.
,,	Fig. 42.	2·8	16 rays.
,,	Fig. 44.	3·7	25 rays.

N.B. The above measurements are approximate, and relate to the xylem only since the limits of the stele are difficult to define in fossil sections.

This table shows that in the smaller plants the form of the woody column is roughly cylindrical, as is also the stele as a whole. But in the larger types, while the stele frequently retains its form, the woody column becomes stellate in section, the number of its rays bearing a rough proportion to the increasing diameter. Nevertheless the xylem itself consists (with the exception of the central medulla where present) of a solid mass of wood, which may be differentiated into protoxylem and metaxylem, but there appear to be no parenchymatous cells generally intermixed with the tracheids. In this compact grouping of the tracheids the Psilophytales and other plants quoted possess a feature that is usual in primitive land plants. The sculpturing of such a solid tract of xylem has the effect of increasing the surface-exposure of its dead tracheidal surfaces to the living tissues that surround it : while the depth to which the tracts of parenchyma or of phloem extend into it may be held as a set off to the absence of living parenchyma included in the tracheidal mass itself.

The facts yielded by the living plants and fossils here examined illustrate those changes of vascular structure which are apt to accompany increasing size in plants that may be held as relatively primitive. The cylindrical stele of the small leafless shoots of *Rhynia* or of *Hornea*, with their solid cylindrical core of tracheids undifferentiated, and undisturbed by the departure of traces to lateral appendages, may be held as presenting a correspondingly primitive type of conducting tract (Fig. 5). In the larger species of *Rhynia*, and in *Hornea* the xylem is still a solid core, but the tracheids are differentiated : those lying centrally being distinguishable by their smaller size from the wider elements of the outer zone.

Within the class of the Psilophytales it is a considerable step to the larger *Asteroxylon*, with its leafy shoots. But in its rhizome a small and simple stele may still be found, with a xylem core only slightly greater in diameter than that of *R. Gwynne-Vaughani* (see K. and L. III, IV, Fig. 29). The large aerial trunks, however, have an expanded stele with stellate xylem, which is even pithed, while there are small leaf-traces in its upper region. But these appear to have no definite relation to the rays of the xylem, being inserted upon them either distally or laterally (Fig. 6). *This suggests that the detail of stellation is not determined by the insertion of the leaf-traces.* So far as the facts relating to *Asteroxylon* extend, it appears that the formation of the rays is a feature independent of them : and the same applies for *Cladoxylon*, and for the leafless *Schizopodium*.

The living Psilotaceæ illuminate this point ontogenetically. In them sections of the same individual, taken in series from below upwards, demonstrate progressive vascular changes which accompany increasing size. They show that the features of stellation or fluting, or of disintegration and medullation of the xylic tract appear independently of the entry of vascular traces from lateral appendages. *These changes are in fact initiated within the enlarging stele itself.* The measurements which Dr. Wardlaw has made for *Psilotum* show that such changes on passing to a stele of larger size have the effect of maintaining a relatively large proportion of surface to bulk of the xylem : and that in point of fact that proportion is considerably higher in the elaborated stele than it would have been, supposing the larger tract of wood had been a mere magnified image of the smaller type. Results such as these, obtained from very primitive organisms, reveal a phase of stelar development in great measure, or even wholly independent of the external morphology of the shoot : but in more advanced and elaborately constructed vascular plants the stelar system is apt to be deeply affected by the insertion of appendages. In passing to these it will be well to bear in mind the experience thus gained from simpler forms ; and to attempt to analyse in them the part played on the one hand by the stele itself, and on the other that due to such modifying influence as the appendages may exercise upon it. But it may be expected that such analysis will present ever increasing difficulty as the shoot itself becomes more complicated, and especially where the appendages themselves are large.

There is nothing new or subversive in this conception of the stele and the vascular tracts generally being *morpho-plastic*, in the sense that they are subject to moulding in relation to size ; and that such change may be independent of the insertion of appendages. The independent modification of the stele, which is perhaps the most striking result of the comparisons contained in this Chapter, finds its best illustration in the root ; and this will be treated in detail in Chapter X. It will there be seen that increase in size is followed by structural results cognate with those which have been seen in the stems of the Psilotales and Psilophytales. In the Chapters which immediately follow this, the Lycopodiales, Filicales, and other Vascular plants will be examined in detail from the point of view here introduced : but any general discussion must be deferred until the facts of the size-relation shall have been described for all the leading vascular types.

CHAPTER III

THE LIVING LYCOPODIALES

SINCE the Lycopodiales include a large number both of modern and of fossil plants, it might appear most natural to treat them chronologically in relation to size, so that the most ancient should illuminate the structure of those now living. But for the present purpose the comparison of successive stages in development of the individual bears a special value, and it is by study of the ontogenetic advance from a simple to a more complex state that the size-relation can best be grasped. In fossils serial sections are rarely available : accordingly living examples, in which these can readily be obtained, will be taken first : and the vascular structure of the fossils will be compared in a later Chapter, in the light of the knowledge thus acquired. The two leading genera of living Lycopods, *Lycopodium* and *Selaginella*, while presenting some features of general likeness in their anatomy, demonstrate somewhat different methods whereby the proportion of surface to bulk of the vascular tissues tends to be maintained as the size increases. It will be an advantage to visualise these distinctions before any general comparison is made. The third genus, *Isoetes*, possesses cambial thickening, and so stands structurally apart from the other genera : its primary vascular structure is so much obscured by the early incidence of the secondary development, that it affords little evidence of value for the present discussion.

LYCOPODIUM

In *Lycopodium* all the most important structural changes on increase in size are intra-stelar, the stele itself retaining its originally cylindrical form. They are all primary : no secondary tissues are formed, though these are a marked feature in the related fossils, as also in *Isoetes*. Thus *Lycopodium* presents a clear-cut example of primary stelar modification with increasing size, offering features for comparison with what has been seen in the Psilotales. The early stages of the sporophyte in various species of *Lycopodium* are so diverse in the constitution of the shoot, and in the number and relation of their leaves, that some variety of the initial stelar structure is to be expected. Holloway, on the basis of a wide experience of the sporelings of the genus, states that the stele is at first either diarch or triarch (Studies of N.Z. species of *Lycopodium*, *Trans. N. Zeal. Inst.* xlviii, 1915, p. 298). The number of protoxylems increases upwards by splitting, so that a tetrarch or pentarch state is attained. From this further developments lead, with a conical expansion upwards, to the well-known radial condition, with numerous protoxylems lying at the periphery of a tracheidal system that is variously moulded according to the habit of the species. It is upon the protoxylems that the minute leaf-traces are inserted, in the sporeling. It has already been widely accepted that in the adult shoot of *Lycopodium* the leaf-trace insertions do not dominate stelar structure, and that there is no obligate relation between their number and that of the protoxylem groups; particularly is this so where the numbers are large. This was first apprehended by Cramer (*Pflanzen-physiologische Untersuchungen*, iii. 1855), and it was verified by Jones (*Trans. Linn. Soc.* vol. vii, 1905). Further, it has been shown from study of the apical meristem that the stele is essentially cauline in origin. Thus it is indicated that the stele of Lycopods is a body more or less independent in character, on the later developments of which the leaf has relatively little influence.

From such early beginnings as show a tetrarch stele Wardlaw has traced in a number of species the increase in complexity of the xylem-tract as the size of the stele increases (*Trans. R.S. Edin.* 1924, vol. liii, p. 503). The details of change are various : but in all there is evidence of branching of the proto-xylem groups so as to produce larger numbers of them as the size increases. There is also progressive extension of the living parenchyma and phloem inwards, so that the tracheidal tissue is broken up into tracts which appear more or less separate as seen in transverse section, though as a matter of fact they form a connected whole by fusing upwards or downwards. Sometimes these tracts appear as irregular parallel plates, and this is particularly so in creeping types, such as *L. alpinum, densum,* and *volubile* : sometimes as a complicated xylem-sponge, the spaces between the tracheidal groups being occupied by living tissue, as in *L. squarrosum* and *cernuum.*

There is no need here to follow out the comparison of these different types of structure into detail, but rather to consider their effect as a whole upon the proportion of surface to bulk in the xylem-tracts themselves. For this purpose Wardlaw selected *L. scariosum* var. *Jussiaei* for special study, as an example which gave a wide range of stelar size. Its sporeling had already been carefully examined by Holloway (*l.c.* 1910, Pl. XXXII, Fig. 3, 1916, p. 297), and by Chamberlain (*Bot. Gaz.* 1917, vol. lxiii). Wardlaw's detailed examination begins from the state where the xylem appears as a four-rayed star, either coherent or disconnected centrally as seen in transverse section : phloem and conjunctive parenchyma fill the bays between the rays of the star (*l.c.* p. 514). Each ray consists of a thin plate of tracheids with a small group of proto-xylem elements forming the distended end of each ray.

The stele is delimited by a cylindrical but rather indefinite endodermis.

The series of seven drawings by Wardlaw are all represented on the same scale, but they are not here an onto-genetic series (Fig. 7). They were taken partly from a

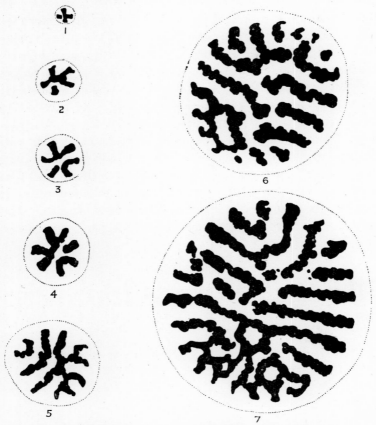

FIG. 7.—*Lycopodium scariosum*, var. *Jussiaei*, Desv. 1, stele of a sporeling (after Holloway) : 2, section from a fine distal twig : 3-7, sections from branches of different thickness. Xylem black : limit of stele dotted. After Wardlaw, *Trans. R.S. Edin*. vol. liii. p. 515, Fig. 5. (× 50.)

sporeling (1), partly from a fine distal branchlet (2), the rest being cut from stems of varying thickness (3-7). Their increasing xylic expansion is so conducted as to avoid any excessive massing of tracheids. The original stellate disposition is thus obscured by sculpturing which follows on increasing size, while each of the apparently detached plates of xylem consists for the most part of only a single row of tracheids as seen in transverse section : all the plates are, however, connected into a continuous system upwards and downwards. Such structure tends to preserve a high proportion of that collective surface by which the tracheids face upon living cells to the bulk of the xylem as a whole. In order to realise the effect of this with some degree of accuracy, Wardlaw has made the necessary measurements and calculations for the actual sections which he has represented. These are set down in his Table II (*l.c.* p. 517), which is drawn up along lines similar to those of Table I, for *Psilotum*. For the detailed explanation of this table reference should be made to the original memoir. Here it must suffice to present his results in a condensed form, as in the adjoining Table IV. The ratio of diameter of the stele to the number of rays again remains approximately constant, but with a tendency to rise as the larger dimensions are reached.

TABLE IV

Table showing ratio of the diameter of the stele to the number of rays of xylem in *Lycopodium*. The measurements are from Wardlaw's, Fig. 5, *Trans. R.S.E.*, vol. LIII, p. 515.

Name.	Number of Section.	Diameter of Figure in mm.	Number of Proto-xylems.	Ratio.
Lycopodium scariosum -	3	19	6	3·16
,, ,, -	4	26	7	3·7
,, ,, -	5	38	11	3·45
,, ,, -	6	66	19	3·47
,, ,, -	7	88	22	4·0

Wardlaw examined the stelar structure in many other species of *Lycopodium* from the same point of view : and he found that the changes of the xylem which appear on passing from a small to a larger size of stele vary in detail,

but are all comparable in one respect : that the larger
stele is never merely the magnified image of the smaller.
The structural changes on passing from a small stele to one
of larger size are consistently such as to maintain a relatively high proportion of surface to bulk of the dead
tracheidal tissue. There is, it is true, a considerable loss ;
but it is very much less than it would have been if the
original outline of the smaller xylic mass had been retained. This result follows from progressive expansion of
the tracheidal tract so as to constitute a xylem sponge of
texture varying with the species, but always connected
throughout : while the meshes of the sponge are filled in
by living tissues. The conclusion follows that this structure
is of physiological importance in securing a due degree of
vitalisation of the xylic tract as the size increases. The
expansion to form a xylem sponge may be held as a special
method of guarding against such a minimum ratio of surface
to bulk as would lead to inefficiency. Survival shows that
a viable balance has been struck, between a minimum of
structural modification and physiological necessity. Of
this *Lycopodium scariosum* may be held as a suitable
example.

SELAGINELLA

The radial species of *Selaginella*, such as *S. spinosa*, P.B.,
are regarded as the more primitive of this large genus.
The stele of the sterile axis is like that of a small *Lycopodium*, except that the protoxylem is at first central and
the endodermis is trabecular. As it enters the strobilus
it expands slightly, and becomes medullated, often with
separate strands of xylem, as is seen distally in the
Psilotaceæ, and a like state appears in the large cone of
Lepidostrobus Brownii (*Ann. of Bot.* vii, p. 329 ; compare
Selaginella spinosa, Ann. of Bot. xxv, Plate XLVII).

Passing from these radial types to the very numerous
species that are dorsiventral, many of which have attained

considerable size, peculiar stelar consequences of the bilateral symmetry are found. The smaller species remain monostelic, each stele being surrounded by its trabecular endodermis. The stele of the sporeling is approximately radial : but as the shoot enlarges upwards the stem takes a dorsiventral form, and the stele itself is flattened, with a thin ribbon of tracheidal wood bearing protoxylems at its two margins. The breadth of this ribbon increases upwards in the larger species, such as *S. grandis*, while its

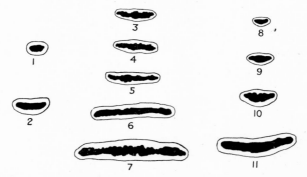

FIG. 8.—1-2, *Selaginella Martensii* : Sections of stele. 3-7, *S. grandis* : 8-11, *S. cuspidata*, var. *elongata*. The stelar ribbon increases in width with size of stem, but remains of uniform thickness. The small sections are basal, the larger distal. (× 27.) After Wardlaw, *Trans. R.S. Edin.* vol. liv, p. 283, Fig. 1.

surface may become corrugated owing chiefly to the enlargement of the individual tracheids : these sometimes form a plate only a single layer in thickness, but frequently it may consist of several layers (Fig. 8). The ribbon-like form, especially where the lateral surfaces are corrugated, offers a much larger proportion of surface to bulk of the wood, as a whole, than if the same mass were cylindrical.[1]

On the other hand, many of the larger species, such as *S. Willdenovii, Wallichii* and *inaequalifolia*, become poly-

[1] Such a ribbon-shaped monostele is not common for vascular plants at large. An example is seen in the fasciated roots of *Caltha*, described by E. H. Moss (*Ann. of Bot.* xxxviii, 1924, p. 789). The roots were abnormally large, and of flattened form. The stele was ribbon-shaped, showing as many as 14 xylem and phloem groups. The wood appears in transverse section as a coherent zigzag tracheal chain, and often it is no more than one series of tracheids in thickness.

stelic as the stem enlarges, and each separate stele may be
surrounded by its own trabecular endodermis. The steps
leading to this in the large climbing species *S. Willdenovii*
are shown for a specific example in Fig. 9, 1-9. All the

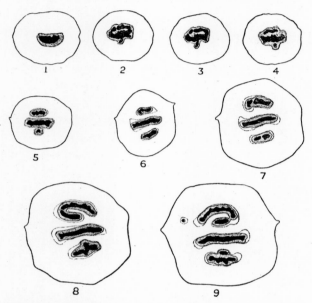

FIG. 9.—*Selaginella Willdenovii*: Sections of the stem   1, from base of
shoot near junction with creeping stem : 2-5, transition to the tristelic state,
showing the method of formation of the dorsal and ventral steles : 6-9, sections
successively higher in the same shoot, showing origin of additional stelar
ribbons. (×9.)

sections came from the same plant, and are drawn to the
same scale : it is apparent that the increasing complexity
follows generally upon the increasing size. The shoot
examined sprang from a creeping rhizome. At the base
it was monostelic with a ribbon-shaped xylem (1). On
passing upwards the stele increased in girth, and changes
appeared which were at first intra-stelar (2-4), leading
further up to the separation of three distinct stelar bands
(5). The ribbon of xylem first becomes wider, and then
its margins curl irregularly so as to enclose an island of
phloem : dorsal and ventral islands of xylem are then

detached, but all are still contained within a single endodermal sheath. Excepting for the shallow involutions of the endodermis the structure of the stele in (4) might be compared with that of a small creeping *Lycopodium*. But the next step is distinctive. The endodermal involutions become deeper, and finally meristeles become independent, each being surrounded by its own complete endodermis, while its xylem is embedded in conjunctive parenchyma and phloem (5-7). With further increase in size elaborations of the dorsal and ventral meristeles of a like nature point towards further segregation, and may result in small additional, but incomplete meristeles, making five in all (8, 9). Meanwhile leaf-traces are given off : most of these arise from the margins of the median meristele, but some of them also spring from the margins of other meristeles as well. This confirms the comparison with *Lycopodium*, where similar irregularity of leaf-insertion occurs, while it also indicates that the developments leading to polystely are themselves independent of foliar influence : in fact that the polystelic state here presents a stelar rather than a foliar problem.

How then should we regard this stelar complication ? Wardlaw's drawings suggest that it is related to increasing size of the stele, though not in exact proportion to the increase of the stem as a whole. That it is so generally for the genus is borne out by measurements of the stems of other species, combined with a statement of the number of meristeles in each. These have been tabulated for 18 species by Wardlaw (*l.c.* No. 2, p. 291). But it is not enough merely to correlate the diameter of the stem with the number of meristeles. In order to gain a rational view of what this peculiar structure implies, it will be necessary to consider the tissues that surround the conducting system. A material factor is probably presented by the firm sclerotic rind of the stem. Internal developments are hide-bound by it. The simple ribbon-shaped stele as seen in *S. grandis* appears as a modification of the protostele by flattening in one plane, a state usual for such monostelic species as are dorsiventral (Fig. 8). Measurements from many monostelic stems show that in none of them does the proportion of width of the ribbon to the diameter of the stem exceed ·45 to 1·0. In the polystelic species, however, the vascular tissue is present in relatively large proportion. If the widths of the stelar ribbons of a large stem of *S. Willdenovii* be added together (as they might be if placed margin to margin), their sum would be considerably greater than the widest diameter of the whole section. In the largest of those measured the ratio of the five meristeles to the diameter of the stem is 1·64 to 1·0. If this large amount of conducting tissue is to be disposed in the form of a thin ribbon, it will need to be convoluted and even broken up to fit it within the encircling rind. This, as suggested by Dr. Wardlaw, appears to give a rational explanation of what is seen, provided the ribbon-shaped stele be adhered to : and this is a form which justifies itself by securing a high surface of presentation of the xylem to the living tissue that surrounds it. In point of fact the principle underlying the changes seen in the large dorsiventral species of *Selaginella* is the same as in *Lycopodium*, viz. to dispose an enlarging body of tracheids in thin plates or ribbons, thereby maintaining a high presentation-surface to living cells. The detailed working out differs owing to the diverse behaviour of the endodermis, and to the presence of the hard peripheral rind that limits the softer cortex in *Selaginella*.

There is, however, within the genus another method of solving the problem, while still preserving a large surface of the xylem, or of the stele as a whole. It is seen in the rhizome of *S. laevigata* var. *Lyallii*, and in a minor degree in *S. uliginosa*. These two species, belonging to distinct sections of the genus, show solenostely and dialystely comparable with that of Leptosporangiate Ferns. In the

rhizome of *S. Lyallii* (as it may be briefly named) the stele
may appear solenoxylic in the very young state (Fig. 10, 1):
but with increasing size the ring expands, and an internal
endodermis gives a typical solenostele (2). With further
enlargement an inner medullary vascular strand separates
(3). This may itself expand, and attain solenoxylic structure (4), a state that vividly recalls that described as polycyclic in Ferns. But this is not all. The upright shoots of
S. Lyallii (and in a minor degree also those of *S. uliginosa*)
present a high degree of segregation of the conducting tract
into separate meristeles : as many as 14 or 15 of them may

FIG. 10.—Steles from rhizome of *S. Lyallii*, uniformly magnified : xylem
black, phloem and parenchyma stippled, dotted line is endodermis. 1,
solenoxylic stele of thin rhizome : 2-4, ascending series of sections of the same
rhizome, showing progressive complexity with increasing size. (× 23.)

be seen irregularly distributed in one section, each with its
peripheral phloem and endodermis : and they continue
thus, but in ever smaller numbers, into the distal twigs
(Fig. 11, 6, 8). These solenostelic Selaginellas thus raise
two problems, that of the solenostelic rhizome and that of
the dialystelic erect shoot. Both present analogies with
similar dispositions in Ferns : the former with such
rhizomes as those of *Dipteris* and *Matonia*, the latter with
stems and petioles of the more advanced Ferns. It seems
highly improbable that there is any phyletic relation that
would explain these structural parallels. A more probable
view would be that they represent homoplastic response
to like conditions.

    In the first place we must enquire into the relation of
the solenostelic to the dialystelic state in the individual

plant of *S. Lyallii* (Lang, *Pres. Address, Sec. K, Brit. Ass.* 1915, p. 11 ; Bower, *Ann. of Bot.* 1911, vol. xxv, p. 566 ; Wardlaw, *l.c.* p. 303). As a rule branches from the soleno-stelic rhizome assume an erect position, and become dialy-stelic: but it has been shown by experimental culture that if the distal end of such a branch is induced to grow as a typical rhizome, the solenostelic state is resumed by fusion of the

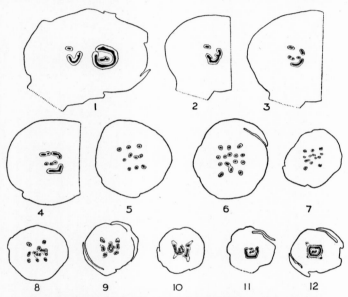

FIG. 11.—*Selaginella Lyallii.* Successive sections from the same stem : drawn to the same scale. 1-6, show the transition from solenostely to dialystely at the base of the erect axis : 7-12 were taken from an erect axis laid horizontally, so as to resume the character of a rhizome. The reversion to solenostely has followed. After Wardlaw.

meristeles. The structural changes may be illustrated by successive sections from a single individual (Fig. 11). The conclusion is that here solenostely is related to the pros-trate growth and dialystely to the erect habit : also that solenostely may be arrived at in two entirely different ways either by expansion of a monostele or by gamostely. A similar conclusion will be seen to apply in the leafless tubers of *Nephrolepis* (see Chapter VIII). Our immediate question will then be whether some size-relation affects or promotes these structural changes. Wardlaw's drawings do not suggest that the origin of the dialystely is directly related to increase in the diameter of the sections (Fig. 11, 1, 2 to 5, 6), though the change to gamostely certainly accompanies diminishing size. But diameter is only one of the dimensions : the basal region of the erect shoot shows signs of active intercalary extension, as indicated by the distant separation of its leaves (Wardlaw, *l.c.* Fig. 15). Moreover, the erect shoot is nutritive and propagative, which the rhizome is not. Intense local interchange between the conducting system and the surrounding tissues, as would be involved in intercalary growth, would demand a due proportion of surface of transit : and this would be efficiently met by a higher degree of segregation of the conducting tracts, which gives a larger surface of exposure in the erect shoot than in the sluggish and soleno-stelic rhizome. This example of such modification does not stand alone : analogies will be drawn later with the structure seen in certain petioles of Ferns, where also inter-calary growth is active (Chapter VII.).

COMPARISON

The peculiar vascular dispositions thus described for *Selaginella* provide material specially valuable in giving insight into the morphology of the stele. The most obvious comparison, as it was also the oldest, is with *Lycopodium*. It was long held that the stele of the latter was the result of a lateral fusion of the separate steles of the largest of the former : and that view survived till quite recent times (Strasburger, *Leitungsbahnen*, 1891, p. 458). It is only mentioned here because it illustrates the danger and incon-sequence of comparing the most elaborate of adult struc-tures in families not very nearly related. Such comparisons should start from the simpler types, and proceed from observation of juvenile states towards the fully adult structure of the most elaborate. If this course be followed for *Lycopodium* and *Selaginella*, it will be found that their comparison will indicate for the two genera divergent lines of amplification of the primary stelar structure. In both genera the axis of the sporeling is traversed by a cylindrical stele with a solid xylem-core : this in *Lycopodium* may appear lobed in transverse section even at a very early stage ; in *Selaginella* also the core is at first cylindrical, and in the radial types it remains so, though slightly fluted upwards. In *Lycopodium* the cylindrical form of the stele itself is maintained throughout, but with varying readjustments of the enclosed xylem-core as the size increases. Those readjustments all tend towards scupturing, by the apparent intrusion of parenchyma and phloem into the xylem-tract. This has the general effect of tending to level up the proportion of the collective surface, by which the tracheal tissue faces upon thin-walled parenchyma, to the bulk of the wood. In carrying this out the tracheids frequently appear grouped in plates or reticula only one row in thickness (*L. scariosum*) (Fig. 7) ; but often the plates consist of several rows (*L. clavatum*). In upright stems there may be an almost uniform xylem-sponge, so constituted that in transverse section groups of tracheids appear isolated, though in fact they are all connected upwards or downwards (*L. cernuum*). Whatever the detail there is never a central pith. The most marked peculiarity of arrangement of the xylem is seen in the creeping types, where horizontal plates of tracheids of varying number pursue a parallel course, with occasional fusions (*L. clavatum, alpinum*). It was with these, which are specialised rather than fundamental types, that the comparisons with large and specialised types of *Selaginella* used to be drawn. Whatever the disposition of the xylem may be, the cylindrical stele of *Lycopodium* is without involution of its convex surface. The leaf-traces may be inserted opposite the protoxylems with some degree of regularity where their number is small ; but where the number of leaves is great their insertions bear no regular relation to the rays of the xylem. From this it is concluded that the moulding of the xylem, to which the isolation of the rays is due, is not defined by the leaf insertions, but is itself a stelar character. In this the independent plasticity of the xylic column of *Lycopodium* corresponds to what has been already seen in the Psilotales and Psilophytales (Chapter II).

The radial types of *Selaginella* share with *Lycopodium* the cylindrical stele, but the endodermis is here trabecular. In the dorsiventral species, however, the stele, while retaining the trabecular endodermis, assumes a flattened form in relation to the plane of branching of the shoot. The xylem appears as a bipolar plate of tracheids, disposed in one to three or sometimes four layers, but without any parenchyma intermixed. The larger the stem and the stele that supplies it, the wider is the flat plate of xylem : it is remarkable how persistently this feature is retained (Fig. 8). All is well so long as the widening is within bounds : but a limit appears to be set where the width of the flat plate exceeds 50 per cent. of the major diameter of the flattened stem. In larger species where the need for conducting tissue is greater, another modification then ensues. The xylic band within the stele first assumes an irregular outline, followed by segregation into bands which lie parallel to one another (Fig. 9). Collectively these may amount in width to more than the diameter of the stem in which they are enclosed, while still retaining their purely tracheidal character. This structure and arrangement of the tracheidal ribbons may be compared with that seen in the creeping types of *Lycopodium* : but the essential difference in *Selaginella* is that there is also involution of the endodermis, so that each xylic band with its envelope of conjunctive parenchyma and phloem is shut off by its own endodermal sheath : thus the stem becomes polystelic, while in *Lycopodium* it is permanently monostelic. The two states thus differing in final results may be held as parallel responses to a demand for maintaining a due proportion of surface to bulk in the enlarging tracts.

A circumstance which probably has its bearing on the difference of stelar behaviour in the two genera is that in *Lycopodium* the inner cortex is as a rule sclerotic, and the stele is thus restricted : whereas in *Selaginella* the inner cortex consists of thin-walled parenchyma, so that amplification is more free until the sclerotic outer cortex is reached. Some degree of initiative probably lies with the peculiar endodermis of *Selaginella*. It will lie with physiologists to consider, from the point of view of radial permeability of the trabecular endodermis, how far the lessening of the surface connecting the stele with the surrounding tissue may have led to involution, which would obviously add greatly to the surface of transit. However this may be, the structural facts show that the methods of stelar adjustment, in relation to increasing size and the maintenance of a due area of transit, have been different in the two genera. They appear as two parallel evolutionary lines, solving each in its own way the problem of stelar adjustment in relation to increasing size.

The solenostelic Selaginellas remain to be considered. The normal origin of solenostely in them is by amplification and medullation of a protostele : this and the progression to polycycly appears to follow the same lines as in Ferns (Chapter VIII). Its result is a notable increase both in the collective limiting surfaces of the xylem and in the area of the endodermis. The further step to the high stelar segregation seen in the erect stems has been correlated with active physiological interchange locally, of which intercalary growth is an index. The converse transition from the dialystelic state of the erect stem, to solenostely where its tip becomes rhizomatous and internodes are shorter, is significant for comparison with the changes at the distal end of the tubers of *Nephrolepis* and of *Equisetum* : but whereas in these the change appears in relation to diminishing diameter of a storage organ, in *S. laevigata* the gamostely appears to be in relation to diminished length of internode.

There is no single genus that shows greater plasticity of the stele than *Selaginella*. A special interest attaches to it since it is microphyllous, and the insertion of the leaf-traces does not control the stelar changes any more than it does in *Lycopodium*. These genera thus provide evidence that the mass of tissue that is called the stele is itself plastic independently of the appendages. It has a right to be treated as a body subject to adjustments related to condition and circumstance. It may be seen to initiate in relation to them such well-known features as medullation, solenostely, dialystely, and gamostely. It is true that these are usually associated with the insertion of appendicular organs, and that, as in the Ferns, where these organs are large they materially affect the result. But the facts relating to microphyllous types such as *Selaginella* show that they do not necessarily dictate it. This aspect of stelar morphology is the natural consequence of comparative study of the living Lycopodiales. It should be borne in mind when studying the forms which vascular tissues assume in megaphyllous types (Chapter VIII).

CHAPTER IV

THE FOSSIL LYCOPODIALES

HAVING now examined the conducting tracts of the living Lycopodiales, which afford the opportunity for comparison of ontogenetic series of sections, and so of tracing directly the structural changes liable to follow in them from increasing size, we may pass to their fossil correlatives. These present a field that differs in one important respect from the living types, in that they include plants which have definitely failed to maintain themselves under conditions of life of periods other than their own : the living genera and species, on the other hand, include only those which have either inherited or adopted structure of survival value. In studying the fossils we should therefore be prepared not only to meet with primitive features, but also to find these sometimes developed, tentatively as it were, to extremes that have proved impracticable. The animal kingdom provides in the great extinct Saurians pregnant illustrations of this in respect of size : and in this the fossil Lycopods may be compared with them. But in either case smaller types of the same class still persist in the living state, and probably existed in the past, side by side with the giants.

In comparing the fossil types an inherent difficulty lies in the fragmentary nature of the material supplied by them. Isolated parts of stems that happen to yield detailed structure give as a rule no clue to their exact position in the plant as a whole. The ontogeny as yielded by successive sections from the same individual is usually wanting, while the structure of the distal twigs which might provide a converse clue to the initial development is almost equally rare. The result is that we are presented with a number of isolated facts, from which it is true that measurements can be taken with a view to tracing the relation of structure to actual size : but inferences drawn from so fragmentary a source cannot be held as equally cogent with those drawn from sections cut at will from living types. Lastly, the data supplied by transverse sections cannot always be tested by reference to longitudinal sections. The result is that the evidence from fossils of the relation of size to structure must necessarily be less convincing than that derived from living plants. In most instances we must needs content ourselves with relatively loose comparisons, and note in them corroboration of the conclusions drawn from the living material, or the reverse. Both the living Lycopods and the related fossils are held to represent relatively primitive structure : those which are still living appear to retain in essentials, though on a smaller scale, the advantages or it may be some of the disabilities of those which have died out. On the other hand, the fossil evidence yields positive data which can only be inferred from comparison of living types : for their stratigraphical sequence gives the opportunity for distinguishing between structure that is primitive and those features that are derivative. Thus their study will often help to differentiate the original structural scheme from its later modifications, and to suggest the relation of these to actual size. For the fossils can be as accurately measured as their living correlatives.

The dendroid Lycopods of the Palaeozoic period raise the question of structural accommodation to large size in a class represented to-day only by small types. Mechanically their axes, which sometimes rose to a height of 100 feet or more, must have been much less effective than those of a Pine or an Oak with their woody columns. As Seward remarks (*Fossil Plants*, ii, p. 95), their power of resistance to the bending force of wind was offered by the stout outer bark, formed of thick-walled elements produced by the activity of a cylinder of cortical meristem ; while the vascular axis, being of insignificant diameter in proportion to the size of the stem, must have played a subordinate part from a mechanical point of view. The existence of a soft middle cortex, usually decayed in the fossil state, may doubtless have linked the more resistant tissues together to form a connected mechanical system : but the whole structure of these large stems, in itself the result of amendments on a primitive type of construction essentially similar to that of the small Lycopods of the present day, must have been ineffective as a mechanical design ; it is better fitted to support a dead weight in still air than to resist the lateral impact of winds. It has proved to be one of Nature's failures, and it need be no surprise that the actual type that became dendroid survives only in a stunted form in the massive stock of *Isoetes*. The vascular system of the fossil Lycopodiales appears in a more favourable light as a conducting system for a shoot of microphyllous type than as a mechanical structure. Its interest will be best developed by first recognising the probable primitive state, and then by tracing the structural amendments imposed upon it. Subsequently these may be compared with what is seen in the modern survivors. In such comparisons special attention must be paid to the changing proportion of the bulk of the tracheidal tissue to the collective surface by which it is in contact with living cells as the size increases.

Comparison points to an origin of the more complicated stelar structure from a simple protostele with a solid core of tracheids that included no parenchyma. Its form was approximately cylindrical, and in all known fossil Lycopods the stem remained monostelic. Upon this the leaf-traces from the numerous microphyllous leaves are inserted with a minimum of disturbance of the xylic tract, and the protoxylems lie at the periphery. The xylem is surrounded by a slender band of phloem, but an endodermal sheath is not clearly defined, though sometimes recognisable. Such a structure with a solid tracheidal column is seen in the stems of *Lepidodendron rhodumnense* and *esnostense* of Renault, and in *L. saalfeldense* Solms, all of which are early fossils : the former from the Culm of Combres, the latter from the Unterculm of Saalfeld. Solm's figures of *L. saalfeldense* show the cylinder of wood solid to the centre, with a smooth outer surface.[1] He records its diameter as 2·5 mm. in a section from the upper end of the conical stem. Renault's drawing of *L. esnostense* (*Flore Foss.* ii, p. 175, Pl. XXXIII, Fig. 2), also depicts a solid woody cylinder with smooth surface, and with centripetal development. The mean diameter of the stem was 15 mm. : that of the woody core hardly 3 mm. Thus these simple and early fossils were relatively small : but Renault specially states that the stems are of variable size (2 to 12 cm. in diameter). Such a structure may be held as representing a relatively primitive state.

This type of structure is subject to modifications more or less clearly related to increasing size. But one characteristic is tenaciously held : viz. that the primary wood, and particularly that peripheral part of it which adjoins the protoxylem, remains purely tracheidal. This is a feature frequently met with in early fossils, but it is rare among living plants : indeed, as has been already stated, no large plant now living has extensive tracheidal tracts without living cells distributed through the mass—either of the nature of pith, or of wood-parenchyma, or of medullary rays. In the fossil Lycopods themselves the changes from the simple primitive structure are such as to increase by various means the collective surface by which the dead tracheids face upon living cells : and these changes are more or less clearly associated with increase in size. The

---

[1] *Pflanzenreste d. Unterculm v. Saalfeld.* Solms Laubach, *Abh. K. P. Geol. Landesanstalt,* 1896, Taf. I, Figs. 7-11.

changes which the primitive xylic column undergoes may be grouped as :—

1. Fluting of the surface.
2. Medullation.
3. Cambial increase, with medullary rays.
4. Segregation of the primary xylem into distinct strands.

Any one of these would have the effect of increasing the proportion of surface to bulk of the dead tracheidal tissue. But they are often combined, and the effect is thus cumulative. It will be seen, however, that the relation to increasing size is not a directly arithmetical one. But it is submitted that the absence of any fixed ratio of size to elaboration does not rule out the advantage derived from the increased cumulative surface, by which tracheids face · upon living cells, in those instances where it clearly exists.

1. *Fluting* of the outer surface of the primary tracheidal column is a frequent feature in fossil Lycopods : The result is to form a ' corona ' of concave crenulations, which obviously increase the surface-area. It is well seen in *L. Harcourtii* (Fig. 12). The first impulse may be to assume that the projecting teeth represent the insertions of the leaf-traces : but though this may be sometimes true, it is not uniform : for instance in *L. selaginoides* the traces do arise directly from the projecting angles (Scott, *Studies*, vol. i, 131) ; but in *L. Harcourtii*, and generally in *Sigillaria*, the traces are given off from the concavities between the projecting teeth. Thus the crenulation appears to be a feature independent of leaf-insertion. This conclusion accords with what has been seen in living Lycopods, and it corresponds also to the structure shown by *Asteroxylon* and *Asterochlaena*. In none of these does the insertion of the leaf-traces bear a constant relation to the detailed contour of the wood. In fact the fluting is a feature of the stele itself.

2. *Medullation.*   In the large majority of the fossil Lycopods the stele is pithed.   Sometimes the ring of primary

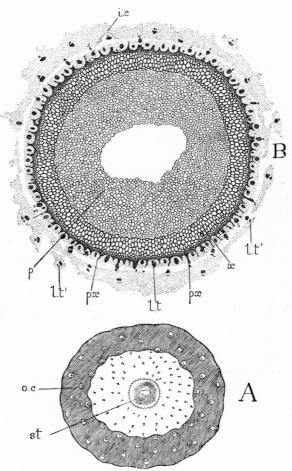

FIG. 12.—*Lepidodendron Harcourtii.*   A, a transverse section of stem :
st =stele : *o.c* =outer cortex, about natural size.   B, stele of the same (× 7):
p =pith, hollow in the middle :   *x* =xylem-ring :   *px* =protoxylem-points :
the leaf-traces join the stele between them :   *l.t* =leaf-trace bundles :
i.c =inner cortex.   Will. Coll. 1594.   After Scott,   The projecting points and
concave hollows of xylem form the ' corona.'

xylem is relatively broad, and the pith small : but frequently the wood forms a narrow band with a massive pith
within, as in *Lepidodendron Harcourtii* (Fig. 12).   The

primary xylem then appears usually as a continuous tracheidal ring. The origin of the pith is intra-stelar, and may be ascribed to conversion of tracheidal cells into thin-walled parenchyma. The ' mixed pith ' of *Lepidodendron selaginoides* is a familiar example of an intermediate state

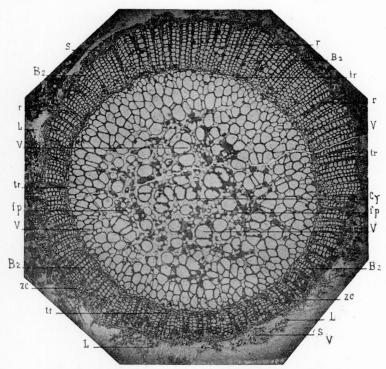

FIG. 13.—Transverse section of stele of *Lepidodendron selaginoides* ; after commencement of secondary thickening, as shown by the zone of radially disposed wood. The primary wood is externally tracheidal only : the central region consists of ' mixed pith ' with reticulate tracheids and parenchyma. After Hovelacque. The lettering at the margin of the blo ·k may be neglected.

(Fig. 13). The details of a mixed pith have been studied by Gordon in *Lepidodendron Scottii*. This early fossil has no secondary wood : in its ' mixed pith ' the parenchymatous cells are short, and are arranged in vertical rows with transverse walls separating the cells. These are accompanied by rows of short scalariform tracheids, especially towards the periphery. Such facts indicate that the pith is of intra-xylic origin by transformation of tracheidal cells (*Trans. R. S. Edin.* xlvi, 1908, p. 445). But in this fossil the medullation varies greatly in bulk at successive points in the same specimen, and without any correspondingly marked difference in diameter of the whole xylic column. The inference here is that the bulk of the pith at any given level is not directly determined by the size of the stele alone. On the other hand, a general comparison of sections of *Lepidodendron* stems shows that such a size-relation does exist, though not in strict proportion : it may even be demonstrated from comparison of sections all taken from the same species : for instance in *Lepidodendron Wun-schianum*. The subjoined table is based on sections of that species in the Kidston Collection in Glasgow University.

TABLE V

	Slide.	Mean Diameter of Primary Xylem in mm.	REMARKS.
Kidston Collection	611	3·43	Primary xylem not uniform to centre.
,, ,,	615	5·0	Not uniform to centre.
,, ,,	890	7·5	Primary xylem differentiated into outer homogeneous and inner more lax zones.
,, ,,	889	20·0	Central tract disorganised probably of pith-character.
Glasgow University Collection	66A	37·0	Massive pith : xylic ring 6 mm. thick, leaving approximately 25 mm. as mean diam. of pith.

It thus appears that the formation of pith in the fossil Lycopods has a general relation to the size of the primary xylic column, but that the relation is not an exact one.

Medullation brings with it an increased exposure of the dead tracheids to living cells, though this would not be as important functionally as increased exposure on the outer surface. Probably other factors than that of size have been operative in determining medullation in those early fossils.

A point of comparative interest is the almost entire absence of pith in the relatively small Lycopods living to-day. There is, it is true, the anomalous case of *Selaginella Lyallii*, which presents so curious an analogy with the stelar structure of Ferns (see p. 36). But the only other examples among living Lycopods of a definitely xylic origin of pith, as in the fossils, are those of the cone of *Selaginella spinosa*, and the primary xylem of the stock of *Isoetes*. In both of these there are signs of a mixed character of the tissue which point to xylic degeneration as the source. In *Isoetes* the primary xylem itself is almost of the nature of a mixed pith. Apart from these, which are quite exceptional, the living Lycopods have secured a viable relation of their enlarging tracheidal tissue with living cells by other means than by medullation : and these appear to have been more effective for life under present conditions, as witnessed by the existence of so many species of *Lycopodium* and *Selaginella* living to-day.

3. *Cambial increase.* In the fossil Lycopods cambial activity results in the formation of a zone of secondary tissue fitting closely outside the column of primary xylem. It may be formed in those relatively primitive types where the primary xylem is a solid core, as in *L. petticurense* Kids ; or in those that are medullated, as in *L. Selaginoides* (Fig. 13). The two features are thus independent of one another. The secondary wood consists of tracheids and medullary rays : the latter are radial plates of tissue including parenchymatous cells : these were presumably alive, as they are in the secondary wood of living plants. The rays extend to the inner limit of the secondary wood, and as in living plants so in the fossils they establish a relation between the

dead tracheids and the living parenchymatous cells. In this there is a sharp distinction between the secondary wood and the primary, which was purely tracheidal. The latter is a construction of limited physiological effectiveness : but the secondary wood with its parenchymatous rays is a structure that, being vitalised, might be extended without limit.

The incidence of the cambial activity is variable. Scott gives a list of six British species of *Lepidodendron* in which secondary wood has not been observed : the best known of these is *L. Harcourtii* (Fig. 12). In seven others it has been seen, but the size of stem in which it appears may vary greatly. In *L. Wunschianum* secondary wood was only found in stems with a primary cylinder 2 cm. or more in diameter, whereas in *L. brevifolium* comparatively small twigs, sometimes with a primary cylinder only 3 mm. in diameter, show a zone of cambial origin (Scott, *l.c.* p. 125-6). On the other hand in *L. petticurense* the result of cambial activity has been seen in a twig with a mean diameter of only ·8 mm. of the solid primary column (Kidst. Coll. Slide, 1053) : in fact secondary thickening of the conducting tract seems to appear irregularly in the fossil Lycopods, as a structural afterthought.

4. *Segregation of the primary xylem into separate strands.* This, though not an uncommon feature of the stele in other classes of plants, and even in the living Lycopods, is rare in the fossils of that class. It makes its appearance locally in certain *Lepidostrobus* cones, and in the stem of relatively late species of *Sigillaria*. A good example of the former is seen in *Lepidostrobus Brownii*, in sections from the upper region of that very large cone (see *Land Flora*, Fig. 175, p. 335). The similarity of this to what is seen in the much smaller cone of *Selaginella spinosa* is striking : in either case the distal fading out of the cauline wood appears to lead to this partial or complete isolation of separate tracts of primary xylem.

Greater interest attaches to the segregation in *Sigillaria*, for here it appears not as a weakening of the xylem in a distal region but in the fully developed axis (Fig. 14). Moreover the change from the concrete and presumably primitive state may be correlated more or less clearly with size, and with geological age. The stele in all of the Sigillarias is in an advanced state of medullation, so that the

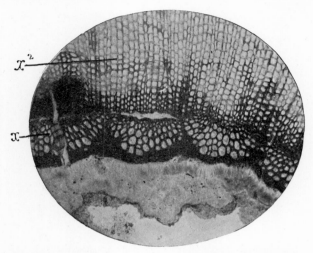

FIG. 14.—*Sigillaria spinulosa.* Part of wood, highly magnified showing separate primary strands (*x*), and secondary wood (*x*²). (× about 18.) After Scott, from photographs by Dr. R. Kidston.

primary xylem appears as a relatively narrow ring of tracheidal tissue at the periphery of a massive pith, often ill preserved. This primary ring of centripetal wood is more or less distinctly crenulated, and the leaf-traces arise from the grooves of the corona (*S. scutellata* as described by Arber and Thomas, *Phil. Trans.* vol. 200, 1908). The secondary centrifugal wood fits closely on the centripetal, and is traversed by medullary rays. It forms a continuous ring, though sometimes it shows signs of division, by slight broadening of the interfascicular rays, into distinct bundles corresponding to the primary strands where these are defined, as they are in *S. Menardi* (see Scott, *l.c.* p. 195).

There is evidence that the segregation of the continuous medullated ring of primary wood characteristic of the older types of *Sigillaria* into distinct strands was progressive in time. This relation was tabulated by Kidston for certain species of *Sigillaria* (*Trans. Roy. Soc. Edin.* vol. xli. 1905, p. 547), and from his table, with some rearrangement and added details, the following has been extracted.

TABLE VI

Name.	Horizon.	Diameter of Primary Xylem in mm.	REMARKS.
S. elegans Brongn. (Kidst. Coll. 964)	Lower Coal Measures.	6·5	Primary xylem, a closed ring with crenulated margin.
S. spinulosa Rost. sp. (Kidst. Coll. 156, 157)	Lower Permian.	9·0	Primary xylem of separate bundles which frequently coalesce.
S. menardi Brongn.	Lower Permian.	16·0	Primary xylem of separate bundles.

This table appears to indicate a direct relation of segregation of the primary wood to size as well as to geological age. But it is necessary to state, as a corrective to such a conclusion, that the relation to size does not hold throughout. For instance, *S. scutellata* Brongn. is a very large plant. As described by Arber and Thomas, the stele is of about the same diameter as that of *S. Menardi* : nevertheless it has a continuous ring of primary wood about 1 mm. in breadth, crenulated but not segregated (*Phil. Trans.* vol. cc, 1908, p. 133). It is of carboniferous age, and that horizon would accord with the absence of segregation : but its large size shows that this is not in itself a determining influence in leading to segregation. Size may, however, have promoted it in the Sigillarians of Permian time ; as it certainly has in other relatively primitive plants, and particularly in the Osmundaceæ, as will be seen later (Chapter VII).

In dealing with the microphyllous Pteridophytes it has not been deemed necessary to take measurements of the leaf-trace strands, or to discuss their detailed structure from the point of view of size. They are as a rule so small, and their xylem appears so uniformly as a simple approximately cylindrical strand, that the influence of the size-factor seems imperceptible in them. The most outstanding exception is seen in the leaves of the genus *Sigillaria*. In *Sigillariopsis sulcata* Scott, and also in the French *S. Decaisnei*, there are two parallel vascular strands which arise from a forked leaf-trace, and traverse the blade longitudinally. Measurements taken from Scott's Fig. 101 (*l.c.* p. 207), and from Hirmer's Fig. 328 (*l.c.* p. 280), show that here the greater diameter, as measured across the two strands in the leaf itself, is less than 1 mm., and that of the undivided leaf-trace in its course through the cortex less than ·5 mm. Such dimensions are small compared with those of many Ferns, but they are large compared with those of most microphyllous Pteridophytes. It is then significant that here the meristele is more complex than in any other microphyllous type. Its segregation into two distinct strands may be regarded as related to its greater size, and to the dimensions of the blade which it serves. It may be compared with what is seen in leaves of *Pinus*. But as Scott remarks (*l.c.* p. 208), an affinity of *Sigillaria* with the Coniferae is improbable. What appears as more reasonable is that in both there is a size-relation, while in both the leaf-form is simple. Of the living Lycopodiales a natural comparison will be with *Isoetes*, which is itself relatively large-leaved. But here the foliar trace is throughout a simple strand, while its xylem is represented only by a few isolated tracheids, doubtless in accord with the habitat of the genus.

COMPARISON

A microphyllous type of vascular plant, with a protostele that never becomes polystelic, and with an inherent
conservatism in respect of its solid tracheidal wood, seems
an unpromising source from which to construct a large
dendroid type that shall succeed both mechanically and
physiologically. And yet, by amendments on the original
scheme that are intelligible from the point of view the size-
factor, it was done in the Palaeozoic period. Naturally the
conducting system, which is the present theme, was only
one factor in the problem of success, but it was an essential
one. We may then consider the changes in the original
plan, which led to the success of the extinct Lycopods at
their own period, and compare them with the changes that
have made the living types succeed at the present day,
though on a smaller scale.

Each of the four methods of elaboration detailed above
(p. 47) results in levelling up the proportion of the collective
surface, by which the dead tracheids are in contact with
living cells, to the bulk of the tracheidal tissue itself. The
effect of them in combination is cumulative as the size
increases. In the most advanced Sigillarias of the Permian
period all four are represented. The result in some of
them is a structure like that so commonly seen in the stems
of Seed Plants, viz. a ring of separate vascular strands
each capable of indefinite cambial increase. The steps
by which such a result as this has been attained from a
simple protostele were not taken simultaneously, nor in
definite order in the fossil Lycopods. Each appears to have
emerged independently of the others : consequently no
clear phyletic sequence can be traced leading from the
simplest to the most complex state.

It may be inferred that the solid primary xylem, without
pith or included parenchyma and without any cambial
activity, was a primitive type for the fossil Lycopods : up

to a certain point it seems to have sufficed for them, as is seen in *L. rhodumnense* and *estnostense*, both from the Culm. In *L. petticurense* from the Calciferous Sandstone of Burntisland there was a solid cylinder of primary xylem, though it is there seen enclosed by cambial wood. In all of these early fossils the outer surface of the cylinder was almost smooth, with no marked fluting ; and in none of the figured specimens was the column of large diameter (1·0 mm. to 3·0 mm.), though larger examples may have existed. In most of those Lycopods where the primary stele is larger its margin is crenulated in section ; that is, it was longitudinally fluted : as in *L. Harcourtii* (Fig. 12). This sculpturing sometimes coincides with the origin of the leaf-traces, but these more frequently arise in the hollows between the projecting ridges : and this is so in the large Sigillarias. Crenulation is in fact a usual feature, and it is independent of leaf-insertion. It may be a question whether the increased surface-area which it brings is of great physiological importance, but there is no doubt that there is an increase of exposed tracheidal surface due to it.

Medullation may be present without cambial increase, as is shown *L. Scottii* and *Harcourtii*. These two innovations appear to be independent in origin. In all the larger types cambial activity is present, which brings a double advantage : not only does it add indefinitely to the woody column, bringing added mechanical strength and conducting power ; but by its medullary rays it provides that feature in which the primary xylem is deficient, viz. an increasingly effective relation between the dead tracheids and living cells. In its origin it may at times be independent of medullation, as *L. petticurensis* shows : nevertheless a relation may be traced between them, for the secondary zone counterbalances the loss of conducting capacity due to medullation, where both occur together. It substitutes an enlarging vascular supply of vitalised wood, that is, with living cells included, for the less efficient non-parenchymatous wood of the primary tract. This is indeed a necessary condition for efficient dendroid development. The very large section of *L. wunschianum* above mentioned (66A. Glasgow Univ. Colln.), with its massive pith and narrow band of primary tracheidal wood, was probably caught at an early stage of this counterbalancing development. At the moment when it was buried in volcanic ash that young stem had only acquired a relatively narrow band of secondary wood ; but the residue of highly medullated primary wood is only 6 mm. in thickness as against a pith-column 25 mm. in diameter.

A similarly narrow ring of primary wood is seen in the large Sigillarias of the Carboniferous period. But in those of Permian Age the ring appears segregated into separate tracts or bundles (Fig. 14). By this not only is a larger proportional exposure of tracheidal surface to living parenchyma secured, but also the parenchymatous pith and medullary rays could for the first time be linked together into a continuous living system. The analogy between this efficiently vitalised conducting tract and that in certain Pteridosperms and Cordaiteæ, and still further with that general in Angiospermic plants, suggests that a common advantage lies in such structural modification where a dendroid habit is assumed. But the similarity of plan has probably had a homoplastic origin. The differences of detail of the plants concerned suggests that a progressive substitution of primary wood by secondary tracts of indefinite development, and the linking up of both by a continuous parenchymatous system, was carried out in a number of distinct phyla, as a physiological condition imposed independently upon them by increasing size. (Compare Scott, ' The Old Wood and the New,' *New Phyt.* vol. i, p. 25.)

It remains to contrast this structure of the dendroid types with that seen in the relatively small survivors of the class. Instead of medullation and cambial increase as the leading changes from the primitively solid tracheidal core, the small Lycopods of the present day have met the physiological demands of increasing size chiefly by per-meation of the woody mass by living tissues of parenchyma, and even of phloem. The extension of living tissue into the tracheidal core seen in *Lycopodium* is a feature essentially similar to the shallow fluting that produces the corona of *Lepidodendron* : in both it is referable in origin to the apical cone itself. But whereas in the fossils this is a minor feature, it has become the leading structural char-acter in *Lycopodium* as the stele enlarges. In itself this is quite an efficient means of enlarging the collective tra-cheidal surface presented to living cells as the size increases, provided the apical meristem be equal to the demand of formation of a primary stele so constructed : and it has sufficed for the largest living species of *Lycopodium*. On the other hand, *Selaginella* has persistently retained the purely tracheidal character of its wood. This suffices for the relatively small trailing shoots of *S. spinosa* : but in the large dorsiventral types its retention has led, by steps of a widening tracheidal ribbon, to that peculiar form of polystely described in the preceding Chapter for *S. Will-denovii*, and referable, as suggested, to folding of the ribbon within a resistant rind. Lastly, in *S. laevigata* var. *Lyallii* stelar modifications appear comparable with what is seen in the Filicales rather than in any other Lycopods.

The result of such comparisons of Lycopods, living and fossil, is to show how plastic the primary stele may be in a Class that is clearly circumscribed and natural, though marked by a strange conservatism. The various modifica-tions and elaborations which appear may all be reasonably re-lated to increase in size. All of them,—but especially those seen in the forms which are living to-day, and so have proved their physiological efficiency,—tend to preserve, as the size increases, a due proportion of that collective surface by which the dead tracheids maintain contact with living cells.

CHAPTER V

SPHENOPHYLLALES AND EQUISETALES

THESE two classes are often included under the general designation of the Articulatae, and for the purpose of the present discussion they are best considered together : for their stems are constructed upon a common plan, a fact that probably has its connection with the verticillate arrangement of their relatively small leaves. As elsewhere in types that are relatively primitive, the vascular construction of the axis is based on the protostele with a solid tracheidal core. This is actually realised in the Sphenophyllales ; and by comparison it may be inferred that the highly medullated state of the Equisetales originated from a like source, though it has only been demonstrated in the sporeling stage of some species of *Equisetum*.

SPHENOPHYLLUM

The known species of *Sphenophyllum* were all small plants with slender ribbed stems, and the ribs ran straight on through the nodes, while the leaves were whorled and superposed, the number in each whorl being a multiple of three. This naturally accords with the triangular core of primary wood, which is a prevalent feature. The primary xylem is tracheidal without parenchyma included in it ; at the angles narrow spiral or reticulate elements are found, their position in the fossil state being often marked by a canal. The three sides of the triangle are concave : in fact the primary xylem has the form of a three-rayed star, and finds its correlative in small branches of *Psilotum*

(Fig. 15) (compare Bertrand, *Arch. Bot. du Nord*, vol. i, p. 410, Figs. 180, 181, p. 437 ; Fig. 186, C). Closely fitting round this xylic core lies the cambial wood, consisting of radial series of wider tracheids : the whole is traversed by parenchyma, not here disposed in consecutive medullary rays, but still the parenchyma constitutes an efficiently connected system of living tissue that traverses the

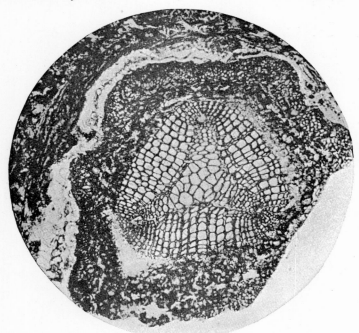

FIG. 15.—*Sphenophyllum insigne.* Transverse section of rather young stem. (×about 30.) After Scott. See Text.

secondary wood. This wood may attain considerable bulk, forming in old stems a massive cylinder, with the primary wood completely embedded in it. The dimensions of the latter are small : for instance, in *S. insigne* the diameter, as measured from one of the protoxylems by a line bisecting the triangle, is about 1·0 mm. others may be larger or smaller, but about 1·0 mm. is the usual diameter of the primary tract of wood in *Sphenophyllum.*

The axis of the strobilus of *Sphenophyllum Dawsoni*
shows a five-rayed star of primary xylem, but otherwise
it has a like structure to that of the vegetative shoot,
though without secondary thickening (Williamson, *Phil.
Trans.* 1874, Pl. V, Fig. 29). The diameter of the xylem
measured as in the vegetative shoot is about 1·25 mm. It
would be a mistake to insist too closely on the higher
stellation as following in this instance on the slightly
greater size, though the facts appear to justify it. But the
size-relation is more significant in the more elaborate
primary xylem of the large cone of *Cheirostrobus*, which
though unique in its complexity, shows analogies of structure with *Sphenophyllum*. There is neither purely parenchymatous pith nor secondary thickening, but the centripetal wood towards the centre of the stele is mixed with
parenchyma, while the number of rays is about 12 : these
correspond in position and number to the sporophylls.
The higher differentiation goes with much larger dimensions than in *Sphenophyllum* for the diameter of the
primary xylem in *Cheirostrobus* is about 2·65 mm. It will
be seen in Chapter X, on roots, that a higher stellation goes
there also with larger size ; but here the question of such
a direct relation is complicated by the presence of appendages, which are absent in roots. The three examples
quoted may be tabulated as below :

TABLE VII

Name.	Source.	Diameter of Primary Xylem in mm.	REMARKS.
Sphenophyllum insigne	Scott, *l.c.* Fig. 42.	1·0	Solid, 3 rays.
Sphenophyllum Dawsoni	Williamson, *Phil. Trans.* 1874, Pl. V, Fig. 29.	1·25	Solid, 5 rays.
Cheirostrobus	Kidston Collection, Slide 84A.	2·65	Mixed pith about 12 rays.

The figures are given here for what they are worth, and the parallel progression of size and stellation should not be too strongly insisted on. Nor would the facts have been stated here at all, were it not that they accord, both as regards structure and the number of rays, with widely spread parallel observations in relation to size in other plants, and in other organs.

EQUISETALES

In the living Equisetales medullation and segregation of the primary stelar system are as prevalent in the adult stem as they are deficient in the Sphenophyllales. It is unnecessary to describe the structure in detail : a reference to the ' Origin of a Land Flora,' p. 385, will suffice, and to the group of Pfitzer's drawings given as our Fig. 16. The vascular strands, corresponding in number and position to the ribs of the stem, all pursue a separate course through the elongated internodes, though fusions with consequent structural complication occur at the nodes. The number of the strands varies with the size of the stem, but without any constant ratio, as Pfitzer's drawings show : it may be as low as three in weak branches, or even two in sporelings : while in the larger species the strands of an adult stem may number over 30. Each presents a primary xylem, the few scattered tracheids of which suggest that the structure is vestigial, and a ' carinal ' canal lies at the central limit of each strand (Fig. 16, B, D, F). A reason for the simplicity of this structure may probably be found in the semi-aquatic habit of *Equisetum* : but such a view involves the presumption that there has been reduction of the primary xylem from a prior condition where it was more amply represented. This presumption is supported by the fact that a protostele with tracheidal core has been actually observed in sporelings of *E. arvense* (Barratt, *Ann. of Bot.* xxxiv, 1920, p. 204) ; it is

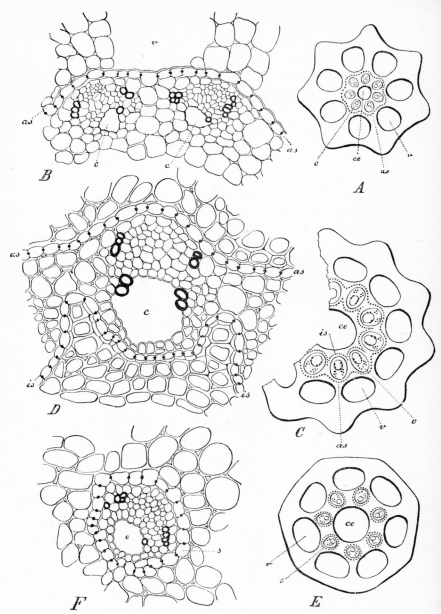

FIG. 16.—A = transverse section of the stem of *Equisetum palustre* (× 26) ; B = part of it × 160. C = transverse section of the rhizome of *E. sylvaticum* (× 26) ; D = part of it × 160. E = transverse section of the rhizome of *E. litorale* (× 26) ; F = part of it × 160. *cc* = central cavity. *v* = vallecular canals. *c* = carinal canals. *s* = sheath of separate strands. *as* = outer. *is* = inner general endodermis. In A, C, and E, the endodermis is indicated by a dotted line. After Pfitzer, from *Rab. Krypt. Flora.*

continuous as such only for a short distance, soon expanding into a soleno-xylic state, and finally disintegrating upwards to form distinct strands. Comparative evidence from an early fossil points towards the same conclusion : for in *Protocalamites petticurensis* from the Lower Carboniferous, a greater representation of primary wood appears than that either in any adult *Equisetum* or in most other Calamites (Fig. 17). In both of these carinal canals occur with the protoxylem elements closely related to them, and abutting

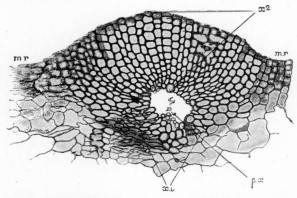

FIG. 17.—*Protocalamites petticurensis.* Transverse section of the xylem of a vascular bundle in the stem. px=protoxylem. x^2=secondary wood. xi=centripetal wood, on the inner side of the canal. mr=medullary rays. ($\times$ about 60.) After Scott.

directly on the pith. But in the Petticur fossil there is also a tract of primary centripetal wood which lies facing the pith, on the side where in other Calamites the canal directly adjoins the pith. This tract of wood is held as vestigial, and if so it would represent a relic of that primary centripetal wood which in *Sphenophyllum* appears as a solid xylic mass, with no pith at all. The inference is that the stelar type of *Sphenophyllum* and that of the primitive Calamarians is the same : and that the highly medullated stele both of *Equisetum* and of *Calamites* was probably derived ultimately from a type with a solid core of primary xylem. Both of them have departed far from that primitive state, but along lines so much alike that the structure

E

of the very young twig of a Calamite is in all essentials
similar to that of an *Equisetum* : also that in the adult
state a Calamite is simply an *Equisetum* with secondary
thickening (Scott, *Studies*, i, p. 21).

In the elucidation of the stelar structure of the Equisetales it is necessary to consider not only transverse enlargement but also longitudinal growth so as to form those
elongated internodes that are so characteristic a feature.
As Miss Barratt has shown (*l.c.* p. 230), the basal plan was
a siphonoxylic stele. In this gaps have arisen owing to
failure of the cells in certain tracts to develop as tracheids.
On this conception it will be seen that the structure met
with in the cone links together the unbroken siphonoxylic
stele of the basal region of the sporeling, and the vascular
structures of the node and internode of the vegetative axis.
The relation of the former to the latter is closer in the
Calamites than in the Horsetails. The view may now be
adopted with some degree of certainty that the sporangio-
phore of the Equisetales is not of foliar nature, but an
organ of a type distinct from that of the leaf-teeth. In
most of the Calamites the sporangiophores are associated
with the leaf-sheaths in the cone : in *Equisetum* the leaf-
sheaths are absent. The further view may now be definitely
held that the state of the latter is due to the failure of
the leaves to develop in the fertile region, and that the
annulus of *Equisetum* represents a last vestigial leaf-sheath
(see *Land Flora*, pp. 382-385, and Barratt, *l.c.* pp. 220-228).

Following the stelar structure upwards from the basal
siphonoxylic stele, and bearing in mind the semi-aquatic
character of the Equisetales, the vascular system of the
vegetative region may be interpreted thus. The node
presents the least altered structure, with its considerable
blocks of purely tracheidal wood, now shown by Miss
Barratt to be due not to cambial activity, but to overlapping of previously existing cells by sliding growth, as
they elongate to form tracheids. This, together with the

readjustments and complications arising from the insertion of leaf-traces, and the vascular supply to the well-known nodal buds and roots, will account for the peculiarly complex nodal state of the Equisetales. The internode in its intercalary development suffers rapid extension, and the internodal state of the separate vascular strands may be held as representing the last stage of reduction of the xylem consistent with a continuous and effective supply of water to the leaves and branches. Thus viewed the tracheids adjoining the carinal canal are the protoxylem, while the outer groups of tracheids right and left of it represent vestiges of the centrifugally developed primary wood of a monostelic system. It is upon this that in *Calamites* a secondary cambial development has been superposed, originating immediately outside the primary vascular system, and joining up with it to form an extended conducting tract.

It may be asked how does this vascular construction stand in relation to increasing size ? It has been seen in other primitive plants that in accordance with the demand for a due proportion of surface to bulk in an exclusively tracheidal wood, the conducting tract is liable to be moulded and finally disintegrated. But in *Equisetum*, or in the young shoot of a Calamite this demand would have no effect : for in them the primary xylem is represented by tracheids either isolated, or disposed in such small groups that each has ready access throughout its whole length to living parenchyma. In *Calamites*, however, the primary wood is succeeded immediately by cambial wood. Here again adequate provision is made structurally to meet the demand of increasing size by the presence of medullary rays with their living cells permeating the mass. The structure of the secondary wood is thus such as to allow of unlimited dendroid development, just as in Seed-Plants : and the Calamites with their large trunks have taken full advantage of it.

Passing onwards to the cone of *Equisetum*, the leaf-sheaths are absent, while the numerous sporangiophores are disposed upon the axis without strict regularity. It has been shown that in the fertile region the primary xylem spreads laterally into more or less continuous but irregular sheaths, interrupted by xylic gaps, which bear no constant relation to the insertion of the sporangiophores (Fig. 18). These gaps also may be regarded as the result of incomplete development of the solenoxylic cylinder : but it is not complicated here by any high degree of intercalary elongation, nor stabilised by the insertion of regularly alternating foliar traces. There is no marked effect of the size-relation, beyond the presence of a voluminous pith lying internally to the tracheidal wood. On the view thus adopted the whole stelar system of *Equisetum* may be based upon a soleno-xylic state of a monostele. The gaps in the wood, whether in the vegetative or the fertile region, are not foliar gaps, but correspond rather to such gaps as those which are called ' perforations ' in the stelar morphology of Ferns.

Fig. 18.—Longitudinal reconstruction of the xylem of cone of *Equisetum giganteum :* axial xylem black, traces and parenchyma white. (× about 7.) After T. M. P. Browne.

Though the conducting tissues in *Equisetum* may themselves be thus exempt from the incidence of the size-relation owing to the simplification of their highly disintegrated xylem, the stelar state may still be affected by it, as is shown by the structure of the tubers, which so often result from the expansion of internodes for purposes of storage. The endodermis is known to be variable in its relation to the individual strands within the genus *Equisetum*. Sometimes it surrounds the whole group, thus delimiting the single stele, as in *E. arvense* and *palustre* (Fig. 16, A, B). In other species there may be in addition an inner endodermis shutting off the inner-lying pith, as in *E. sylvaticum* (C, D) : in others again each vascular strand may be surrounded by its own sheath, as in the rhizome of *E. hiemale* (E, F). In this connection the structure of the tubers of *E. arvense* is interesting, for it shows that here there is a size-relation. As the internode swells to form the tuber the vascular strands spread widely apart, and each becomes surrounded by its own endodermal sheath, as in the rhizome of *E. hyemale.* But as the tuber contracts again towards the next node, the strands approach in a narrowing ring, and the original structure is resumed, with the general endodermis surrounding them all (Fig. 19). An expansion of the circle to about three times its original diameter, and a

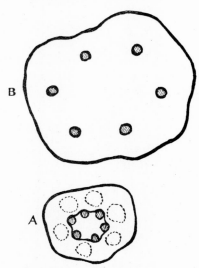

FIG. 19.—*Equisetum arvense.* A =transverse section of internode of rhizome, 1 mm. in diameter. B =transverse section of tuber, to the same scale, showing a ring of meristeles, each with its own endodermis. 3 mm. in diameter. (× 10.)

subsequent contraction accompanies or perhaps dictates the structural change. A similar size-relation exists in the tubers of *Nephrolepis* (see Chapter VIII). These instances of a size-relation of the endodermis, and the part which it takes in the segregation of meristeles, lead on to others such as those already noted in *Selaginella.* They find their analogy in the meristelic structure so prevalent in the Leptosporangiate Ferns, and occasionally in certain large roots, as in the polystelic tubers of *Orchis* (see Table XXIV, p. 176). These will be considered together in a later chapter.

From this brief sketch it will appear that the Articulatae take no crucial place in our comparisons of structure in relation to size. There is too little indication of gradual steps between the two distinct types of the definitely protostelic Sphenophyllales, and the Equisetales with their highly disintegrated stelar structure. The cambial developments in each are *ex post facto*, as regards the primary structure, and being permeated by living parenchyma do not greatly affect the immediate question. But the facts relating to the primary structure, so far as they go, are in accord with the conclusions derived from other sources : for we find the solid tracheidal masses of primary wood in the adult stem of *Sphenophyllum* are relatively small, and with few rays : but the larger primary xylem tract of *Cheirostrobus* has a many-rayed star, with mixed pith internally : while those of the Equisetales have their xylem so greatly reduced in relation to their semi-aquatic habit, that this in itself has resolved for them any problem of size in relation to their primary conducting tracts.

CHAPTER VI

THE FILICALES. COENOPTERIDACEÆ

WE pass now from the Microphyllous Pteridophytes—designated by Jeffrey as the *Lycopsida*, diagnosed by him anatomically by the absence of foliar gaps, and described as ' cladosiphonic,' to the megaphyllous forms—designated by him as *Pteropsida*, distinguished as possessing foliar gaps, and described as ' phyllosiphonic.' The megaphyllous Pteridophytes are known as the *Filicales*, or *Ferns*.[1]

A common structural feature, already noted for the most primitive microphyllous types, appears also in the most primitive of the Filicales : viz. that the primary wood is purely tracheidal. It will be seen to be characteristically so in the Botryopterideæ, and in the fossil Osmundaceæ, while it survives in the living *Osmunda*. But as in the microphyllous types this simple structure has been seen to pass over to a vitalised state, so also in the Filicales evidence will be advanced to show that while purely tracheidal primary wood was certainly primitive, a progressive ' vitalisation ' was achieved also in them, though

---

[1] Professor Jeffrey's anatomical distinction is open to very significant exceptions. Many adult Ferns of primitive type, and many sporelings of living Ferns have no foliar gaps. The existence of this structural feature appears to depend not upon phyletic origin, but upon the establishment of a certain size-relation of the leaf to the axis that bears it, which works out as a disturbance of the axial structure by departure of the trace. This relation is absent in the most primitive Ferns, though it is established as a rule in relatively advanced types. Similarly it is absent in the sporelings of Leptosporangiate Ferns, but is established as the sporeling forms successively larger leaves, and as consequently the disturbance caused by the departure of their traces becomes proportionately greater. It is, in fact, a phenomenon of size and proportion rather than an inherent racial character. Naturally, if this is so, foliar gaps might be expected to appear in megaphyllous rather than in microphyllous types, though not inherently characteristic of either.

71

with variety of detail. It is the underlying principle that is important, viz. that structural changes, such as meet the contingent loss in area of presentment of dead conducting tissue to living cells, are seen to accompany increase in size in both microphyllous and megaphyllous Pteridophytes.

The latter possess one very important feature that enhances the interest they present in relation to size above that of microphyllous types. It is that the leaf as it increases is subject to the same requirements according to size as the stem that bears it : and being relatively large it meets them by structural changes of the same order, though not like them in detail. There are then in the shoot of the Filicales two lines of comparison in respect of size and structure, instead of only one as in the microphyllous types. It will be shown that such changes in the stele of the axis and in the meristele of the petiole progress, with increasing size of each, more or less independently, though along parallel lines. In so far as their structural changes are similar, and produce analogous results in solution of their respective size-problems, the evidence may be held as cumulative in supporting the general thesis of structural adaptation to increasing size.

COENOPTERID STEMS

The Coenopteridaceæ are Ferns known only in the fossil state. The small cylindrical stem of *Botryopteris cylindrica* is often well preserved, showing in transverse section its cylindrical protostele with a solid core of tracheids, the protoxylem lying centrally, and the whole surrounded by peripheral phloem (Fig. 20). A similar structure appears in other species of *Botryopteris*, also in *Tubicaulis* and *Grammatopteris*. It is important to realise how small these stems, and particularly their solid woody cores actually are. That of *Tubicaulis Sutcliffii* is stated to be about 2 mm.

across : but that of *B. cylindrica* is much smaller, the stem
being 1·6 mm. in diameter, and the stele only 0·8 mm.
We there see what is probably a very primitive type of
stele represented from the Culm onwards. It is this type
of stele that appears on a small scale in the stem of the
sporelings of living Ferns. In most Ferns this simple

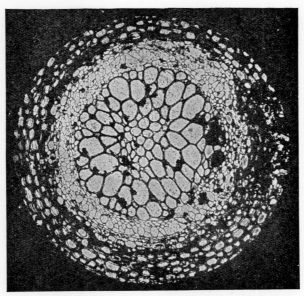

FIG. 20.—Transverse section of a stele of *Botryopteris cylindrica*, showing
a protostele with a solid core of xylem, and peripheral phloem. The endodermis is not clearly shown is this fossil Fern.

structure is departed from in the adult : but in many
genera of relatively primitive Ferns of the present day the
protostelic structure persists, though with this structural
modification, that the wood is there permeated by living
parenchyma (Chapter VIII).

When the stele attained larger dimensions, as it did in
certain of the Coenopterids while still retaining the protostelic state, it may take a modified form. For instance, in
Ankyropteris Grayi (Fig. 21, 2, 3), which is 2-3 mm. in
diameter, it is corrugated, the insertions of the leaf-traces

projecting and the surfaces between them being hollowed : moreover the curvatures of the hollows are apt to be deeper in the larger than in the smaller specimens, though there appears to be no strict numerical relation in this (3). A more extreme example is seen in the stele of

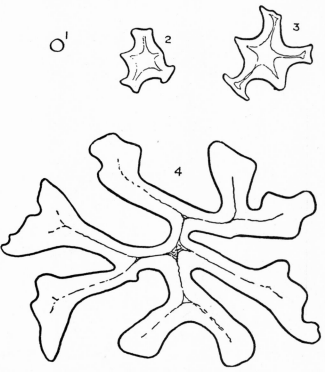

FIG. 21.—Outlines of the xylem of Coenopterid steles, all drawn to the same scale, to show their relative sizes (× 5). 1 = *Botryopteris cylindrica*. 2 = *Ankyropteris Grayi*. 3 = ditto, larger. 4 = *Asterochlaena laxa*. The elaborateness of outline increases with the size.

Asterochlaena laxa, which may be as much as 15·5 mm. in diameter (4). In this Fern the stele itself is thrown into deep involutions of the surface : for though the outline shown represents the wood only, the bast and apparently the endodermis also follow its form, so that the stele and not the wood only is moulded into a complex figure. Centrally there is a region of ' mixed pith,' with wide storage-tracheids dispersed through the parenchyma, while narrow tracheids representing protoxylem are deeply immersed in the metaxylem.

Such fluting or involution of the stele, and of the xylem in particular, follows essentially the same method as that seen in *Asteroxylon*, and in certain species of *Lycopodium* ; and it has the same effect in tending to maintain a due proportion of surface to bulk. But in them it is only the xylem that is fluted, here it is the stele itself, for the outer sheaths follow the curves of the wood. The relation of the leaf-insertions to the fluting of the stele or of the xylem is substantially the same in both. Where the stele is relatively small, as in the thinner shoots of *Lycopodium* or in *Ankyropteris*, the leaf-traces are inserted on the projecting flanges (Fig. 21, 2, 3). But in the large *Asterochlaena*, as in the larger shoots of *Lycopodium* and in *Asteroxylon*, where the number of leaves is large and their arrangement complex, there is no strict relation between the individual leaf-insertions and the rays of the star. Such facts shared by plants of so distinct affinity, are significant : they indicate that the fluting or stellation is a feature inherent in the stele itself : they support the view that stellation is adaptive according to the size of the stele, and may be carried out independently of the leaf-insertions (Fig. 21, 4). A further example of stellation is seen in the ancient *Asteropteris*, from the Upper Devonian of New York State (see Scott, *l.c.* p. 310, Fig. 139). It was a relatively large plant, with a stem 2·5 cm. or more in diameter, containing a stele with xylem coherent at the centre, but extended outwards into about 12 xylic plates : from the margins of these clepsydroid leaf-traces depart to supply the super-imposed whorls of leaves. It is held to be of Filical alliance. There is reason to believe that all of the stems with stellate structure which have been described here were upright in position when alive.

The facts and approximate measurements for these Coenopterid plants may conveniently be condensed into tabular form, thus :

TABLE VIII

Name.	Authority.	Diameter of Stem in mm.	Diameter of Stele (or of Xylem) in mm.	REMARKS.
Botryopteris cylindrica	Scott, *Studies,* Fig. 156.	1·6	·8	Creeping : solid cylinder of xylem.
Ankyropteris Grayi	Scott, *Studies,* Fig. 130.	17·5	3·75	Upright (?) : xylem differentiated and fluted : five projecting flanges.
Asterochlaena laxa	Bertrand, *Monograph,* Fig. 22.	30·0	15·0	Upright (?) : xylem deeply stellate, and differentiated : eight projecting flanges.
Asteropteris noveboracensis	Scott, *Studies,* Fig. 139.	25·0	15·0	Upright (?) : xylem stellate, apparently not differentiated : about twelve flanges.

The measurements given in this table are all approximate rather than exact, though they are based upon the best sources. They appear to bring out a proportional relation between stellation and size : but it must not be assumed that any constant proportion rules ; exceptions can readily be found. For instance, in *Clepsydropsis australis* described by Mrs. Osborn (*Brit. Assn. Report*, 1815, p. 727), and by Sahni (*Phil. Trans.* B, vol. ccxvii, p. 1, 1929), though the stele appears to be 5 mm. or more in diameter, and has the form of a 5-rayed star as in *A. Grayi*, it has less acute points though it is actually of larger size (see Scott, *l.c.*

p. 305). Nevertheless the extreme forms show that a loose relation does exist in Coenopterid Ferns between size and stellation ; and it is of the same nature as that in the microphyllous Pteridophytes described in Chapters II to V.

In other Coenopterids, which there is reason to believe were of creeping habit, a change is seen in the solid woody core in the direction of a ' mixed pith ' : and it appears without fluting either of the xylic column or of the whole stele. This has been demonstrated in the rhizomes of *Diplolabis* and of *Metaclepsydropsis* by Gordon (*Trans. R. S. Edin.* vol. xlvii, p. 711, and vol. xlviii, p. 163). In both of these the xylic core is larger than that seen in *Botryopteris* ; the diameter in the latter is 1·5 mm. that of the former 3·5 mm. as against measurements of less than 1·0 mm. in *Botryopteris*. But the structural advance in the two genera is not in direct relation to size : for the larger, viz. *Diplolabis*, has only short reticulate tracheids at the centre, and there is no parenchyma : the smaller type, viz. *Metaclepsydropsis*, has parenchyma centrally, forming with the tracheids a ' mixed pith.' Both, however, show structural advance on what is seen in the much smaller stele of *Botryopteris* : and that is a fact of greater importance than the degree of reaction in each to size.

There is yet another type of Zygopteridean stem, in which the problem of increasing size is met by modification of structure along more modern lines, viz. by cambial activity. Signs of this have been seen in *Metaclepsydropsis* (Gordon, *l.c.* Fig. 46) : but in *Botrychioxylon* a zone of secondary wood with parenchymatous rays surrounds the primary core (Scott, *Studies*, p. 319). The structural comparison with a modern *Botrychium* is fully justified. In both the size-problem is adequately solved by the presence of living cells permeating the conducting tract. They thus possess the key to unlimited growth like any modern Seed-Plant : but neither the Coenopterids nor the modern

Ophioglossaceæ seem to have fully realised the opportunity offered by cambial thickening (Fig. 22. For a more full discussion of this structure see Chapter VII, p. 91).

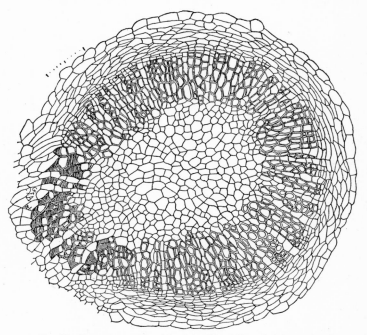

FIG. 22.—Transverse section of the stele of *Botrychium virginianum* showing a massive pith, the primary xylem being vertigial. The radially disposed tracheids and the medullary rays are evidence of cambial activity, which has produced the secondary wood. After Atkinson   (× about 72.)

STAUROPTERIS

That problematical plant *Stauropteris* may best be introduced here, in a non-committal position between Coenopterid stems and petioles ; for it is still uncertain to which category the stalk of this shrubby plant belonged. It appears as an interesting example of the relation of size to structure, presented by an erect cylindrical part. Tansley's well-known drawing may serve as an illustration of the vascular structure of the main rachis (Fig. 23). The single vascular tract measures rather over 1·0 mm. in mean

diameter.   The wood appears cruciform in section, being
composed of four purely tracheidal wedges often united
at the centre ; but they may be more or less detached.   A
protoxylem group lies near the peripheral margin of each,
whence the supply for the successive pairs of pinnae arises.
Phloem with large sieve-tubes surrounds the wood, and
intrudes inwards wedge-like, often extending to the centre
so as to interrupt its continuity.   The stelar structure thus

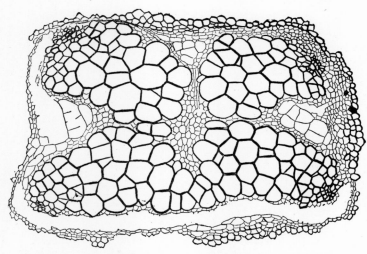

FIG. 23.—*Stauropteris oldhamia.*   Transverse section of the vascular tract
of a main rachis, showing the cruciform wood, with protoxylem near the four
angles.   Large sieve tubes are seen in the bays of the wood, and small-celled
phloem between the wood and the cortex, and in the middle.   (× 60.)   From
Tansley, *New Phytologist,* after Scott.

compares with that in the stem of some species of *Lycopodium,* but more nearly with that of *Asteroxylon* (Fig. 6).
In all of these the dead woody column is invaded and even
disintegrated by living tissue, with an increased surface
of presentment as the result.   Such comparisons are closer
than with any Fern petiole.

In point of actual size the woody column of a large stalk
of *Stauropteris* (about 1·1 mm. in diameter), falls between
that of the small oval column of *Hornea* or *Rhynia,* and the
stellate tract of *Asteroxylon Mackiei* (1·8 mm. Fig. 6,

Ch. II). It thus appears that as regards the size-relation the moulding of its purely tracheidal wood is of the same order as in these ancient plants. Whatever systematic position may ultimately be assigned to *Stauropteris*, its conducting tract appears to follow the type of the microphyllous Pteridophytes rather than that of the Filicales.

PETIOLES

Among the Coenopterideæ relatively small and simple petioles are found in *Botryopteris* : but even there some elaboration of form of the tracheidal tract may be seen, especially in those of larger size and later horizon. Notes based upon reliable authority are condensed into the subjoined table :

TABLE IX

Name.	Authority.	Diameter of Meristele in mm.	Remarks.	Horizon.
Botryopteris antiqua	Seward, Fig. 307.	·7	Meristele simple, oval.	Culm Estnost. Calcif. Sandstone.
Botryopteris ramosa	Scott, Fig. 150.	1·75	Three shallow adaxial flanges.	Lower Coal Measures.
Botryopteris forensis	Bertrand, Fig. 26.	2·7	Three deeply cut adaxial flanges.	Permo-Carboniferous.

The facts suggest a progression in time, size, and structure. The earliest types from the Culm onwards are smaller, and they have a petiolar meristele of a simple oval transverse section. But the Permo-Carboniferous species *B. forensis*, has a larger petiole, and the tracheidal tract is deeply grooved along its abaxial surface. *B. ramosa* takes a middle position in size and structure, with its three shallow flanges. The modification of form is such as to provide a greater proportion of surface to bulk in the tracheidal tract than it would have been if the wood had

been simply enlarged, with its form as in *B. antiqua.*
Whether or not there was actually a progression in respect
of size with time, the measurements show a relation of form
to size in the instances quoted. More striking examples of
this are, however, seen in Zygopterid petioles.

One of the most beautiful and convincing statements of
evolutionary progression, based on ontogeny as well as on
comparison, is that advanced by Kidston and Gwynne-
Vaughan relating to the evolution of the petiolar trace
in primitive Ferns. It was founded on their study of the
successive stages that actually existed in *Thamnopteris*, and
many of these may be seen included in a single section of
that magnificent fossil. Their comparison was extended
so that even the most elaborate structure presented by
Zygopterid petioles was brought into relation with the
simple basal region of the leaf-trace of that primitive
Osmundaceous type (Kidston and Gwynne-Vaughan, *Fossil
Osmundaceæ*, iii, iv ; *Trans. R. S. Edin.* vol. xlvi, p. 651,
vol. xlvii, p. 455). But Kidston and Gwynne-Vaughan
omitted questions of size from their discussion : this does
not in any way diminish the value of the comparisons which
they drew : but if actual measurements be made of the
objects dealt with by them, a rational line of causality is
disclosed that may aid the interpretation of these strange
structures.

The Zygopterid petioles include some of the most complex
meristeles that are known in leaves. An example of one
of the largest is seen in *Ankyropteris Westphaliensis* (Fig. 24),
where the continuous conducting tract measures about
6 mm. in diameter with its xylem composed for the most
part of purely tracheidal wood. It has the form of a
' double anchor,' as seen in transverse section. A curved
middle band connects at its extremities right and left with
four ' antennae,' which are curved so as to constitute an
almost complete circle, but this is interrupted on either
side in the median plane. Phloem closely invests the

F

xylem. An interesting fact from the point of view of size, in this and other large meristeles, is that a delicate parenchymatous tract within the xylem of the antennae separates an external band of small tracheids from the mass of larger tracheids within : but both connect at the four margins of the antennae, and there the protoxylem lies.

Such a complex structure as this presents a morphological problem the solution of which may be approached

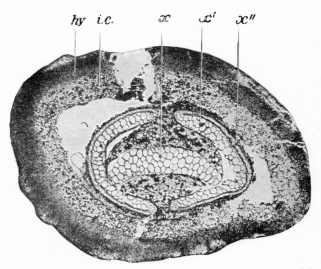

FIG. 24.—*Ankyropteris Westphaliensis.* Transverse section of a petiole showing the double-anchor form of Veristele. *x*=middle band of xylem (' a—polar ') : *x'*, the main lateral bands (' antennae ') : *x''*, the small-celled external arcs of xylem (' filaments ') : the protoxylem lies between *x'* and *x''* : *i.c*=inner cortex : *hy*=sclerenchymatous hypoderma (× 7). After Scott.

along three lines of enquiry : (i) the ontogeny, (ii) comparison with related forms, and (iii) the size-relation. All Zygopterid petioles are founded upon a common type, viz. an elliptical trace with immersed protoxylems at the two foci. It will here be unnecessary to give the whole argument upon which this conclusion is based : a reference will suffice to Memoir IV of Kidston and Gwynne-Vaughan, where the comparisons under heads (i) and (ii) are fully developed. (*Trans. R. S. Edin.* vol. xlvii, 1901, p. 472.

An abstract of their argument is given in *Ferns*, vol. ii, Bower, p. 25), The interest here will lie in (iii), the size-relation of the more complex to the simpler types. The subjoined table gives details for a number of Zygopterid petioles.

TABLE X

Name.	Authority.	Diameter of Petiole in mm.	Diameter of Meristele in mm.	Ratio of Petiole to Meristele	REMARKS.
Dineuron ellipticum	Kidston, *Trans. R.S.E.* 1908 Pl. XLVI. Fig. 1.	2·3	·8	3 : 1	Meristele simple oval with polar loops.
Asterochlaena laxa	P. Bertrand, *Memoir*, 1911, Pl. III, Fig. 13.	6·5	2·0	3¼ : 1	Meristele simple oval with polar loops.
Metaclepsydropsis duplex	Bertrand, *Progressus*, Fig. 7.	9·0	2·0	4½ : 1	Very broad clepsydroid.
Etapteris Scotti	Bertrand, *Progressus*, Fig. 111.	6·15	2·3	2⅔ : 1	Compact double anchor.
Ankyropteris corrugata	Seward, Fig. 315.	—	2·85	—	Wide double anchor.
Diplolabis Römeri	Gordon, Fig. 42.	—	5·0	—	Large clepsy-droid.
Ankyropteris Westphaliensis	Scott, Fig. 135.	11·5	6·3	1·8 : 1	Large double anchor.

All these Zygopterid petioles share an essentially similar type of structure, and they are here arranged in sequence according to the diameter of the meristele. If we compare the extremes of the table the contrast is a broad one. *Dineuron* is relatively small with a meristele of simple form, the tissues of which are concentrated centrally (see Fig. 25, 14) : *A. Westphaliensis* is relatively large with a meristele of very complex form, the tissues of which are decentralised, though still connected by means of a central bridge (Fig. 25, 9). The rest take their places structurally between these two extremes, both as regards actual size of the petioles and the form of the conducting tracts. The conclusion follows that in general a greater elaboration of meristelar structure accompanies increasing size, and though not with exact proportion in each instance it follows parallel lines. That elaboration is such as will level up the proportion of surface to bulk in the xylic tract. In particular the tendency is towards thin plates of xylem rather than towards solid masses, as a comparison of the

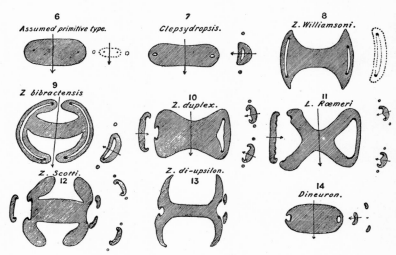

FIG. 25.—Diagrammatic comparison of the various types of Zygopteridian leaf-trace : after Kidston and Gwynne-Vaughan. (*Trans. R.S. Edin.* vol. xlvii, p. 472.) The figures are not drawn to the same scale.

outlines of the diagrams in Fig. 25 shows : but in comparing these it must be remembered that the figures there seen were not drawn to the same scale, as reference to the measurements in Table X will clearly show.

Two further points emerge from this comparison. The first is that while in the smaller types, such as *Dineuron* and *Clepsydropsis*, the wood consists of tracheids only, excepting for the parenchymatous islands of varying size which accompany the protoxylem ; in the largest types, such as *A. corrugata* or *Westphaliensis*, a broad sheet of parenchyma intervenes between the inner and outer bands of the tracheids that form the ' antennae.' They appear

as clear areas in Fig. 25, 8, 9.   From the point of view of size
these facts are important : for the parenchymatous tracts
are largest in the larger types.   They provide an added
surface of presentation of dead tracheidal tissue to living
cells.

The second point is that the tracheidal tract, while
maintaining its continuity, is decentralised as the size
increases.   A comparison of the elliptical meristele of
Dineuron with the almost complete peripheral ring of *A.
Westphaliensis* shows how the bulk of the conducting tissue
is compact and central in the small type, but it appears as
an almost complete peripheral ring in the larger.   The
result is conveyed by the reduced ratio of the diameter of
the petiole to that of the meristele in the largest types (see
Table X).   It will appear later in Ferns how, both in
rhizomes and petioles, this more peripheral disposition of
the primary conducting
tracts is prevalent where
the size is great.   Probably it has its own bio-
logical significance apart
from the adjustment of
the proportion of surface
to bulk.   A further feature
of interest in this con-
nection, which can only
be mentioned here, is

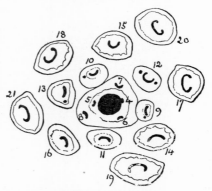

that in certain fossil
Ferns, such as *Tubicaulis*
and *Anachoropteris* which
have been on that account

FIG. 26.—Transverse section of shoot of *Tubicaulis solenites* Cotta, after Stenzel, showing stem
with protostele and the last four leaf-traces
included in the cortex.   The leaves are numbered
in their succession.   The drawing is simplified by
omission of the roots.

styled the 'Inversicatenales,' a similar decentralisation
is attained : but there it results from curvature of the
expanded meristele so that its convex surface is adaxial,
while in most Ferns it is abaxial (Fig. 26).   There are thus
three ways by which decentralisation has been achieved

in large petioles of Ferns : by adaxial curvature, by abaxial curvature, and by forming ' antennae.' Such facts suggest that there is some positive advantage in decentralisation.

It is important to note how the individual leaf-trace expands from the base upwards. This has been already demonstrated by Kidston and Gwynne-Vaughan for the fossil Osmundaceæ, particularly in *Thamnopteris* (K. and G.-V. *Foss. Osm.* iii, Pl. I). A similar expansion may be traced in the Zygopterids : it has been shown by Gordon in *Diplolabis* how the individual leaf-trace widens out upwards, having at first the structure characteristic of the simpler types, and that this expands later into the fully constituted meristele of the genus (*Trans. R. S. Edin.* vol. xlvii, pp. 720-726, Plates II-IV). Such evidence is invaluable in supporting comparisons of the adult state, and relating the elaboration of the meristele directly to increasing size.

COMPARISON

From the descriptions thus given of the structure of Coenopterid Ferns in relation to increasing size certain features emerge which they possess in common, though all of them are open to exception. The first is the prevalence even in the adult of *purely tracheidal* wood. Nevertheless parenchyma may be included in it, in relatively large examples such as the stems of *Asterochlaena* and *Diplolabis*, or the large meristeles of Zygopterids. A second feature is the prevalence of *coherent conducting tracts*, as against segregation. This throws an obligation for the maintenance of a due proportion of surface to bulk upon the moulding of the coherent tracheidal masses into more complex forms as the size increases. A third feature is the *absence of cambial increase*, except in some few examples : and in these its advantage has not been realised to the full. By such features the Coenopterids show their relatively primitive character : consequently they offer a better field for comparison of their primary tracts with those of the microphyllous Pteridophytes than they do with more advanced Ferns.

Perhaps the most remarkable comparison of all is between the structure of the stalk of *Stauropteris* and that of *Asteroxylon*. Well developed specimens of the two do not differ materially in size. The degree of similarity in detail is impressive, not merely in the number of the woody flanges but in their tissue-relations. The moulding of the purely tracheidal wood may even lead in both to an irregular disintegration of the four flanges centrally. The resemblance in these details to some species of *Lycopodium* is also notable, though in these the actual size is much less. In view of the many instances at hand of stellation of the primary xylic tracts in relation to size, such likeness may be only homoplastic : we shall be on safe ground in accepting the stalk of *Stauropteris* as another example of this. How far the structural similarity of its stele to that of *Asteroxylon* indicates affinity is a question that does not enter into the present discussion.

Botryopteris takes a peculiarly interesting place in the study of the size-relation in these primitive Ferns : for in this small Filical type a state exists that is little affected by it. The stele of the stem contains a solid cylindrical xylem-core, usually less than 1·0 mm. in diameter. The petiolar trace in the smaller and earlier species is essentially like it : but in the larger and later species it is marked by three adaxial flanges. The presence of these flanges only on one side of the dorsiventral meristele may be compared with the stellate flanges so often seen in radial axes, in that both are means of giving an added surface of present-ment of the dead tract of wood to the living tissues that surround them : and both occur, not in the smallest examples, but where the size is relatively large.

The difference between stem and leaf of *Botryopteris*—the latter modified in relation to size, the former remaining cylindrical—foreshadows that divergence of development of the two parts which is characteristic of the Zygopterids. These, however, grew to much larger dimensions, and attained highly elaborate structure. Those of them in which the upright stem is large have solved their size-problem by the method of stellation or fluting of the xylic column : and in some instances at all events the phloem and endodermis followed its involutions (*Asterochlaena*). Moreover, the wood itself was differentiated so as to form a ' mixed pith.' The method here as regards the xylem-core is essentially the same as that which has been seen in the stems of *Asteroxylon, Psilotum, Sphenophyllum,* and *Cheirostrobus.* It appears as though the xylem-core were the dominant factor, while the phloem and endodermis are passive : in particular the endodermis may either retain its cylindrical outline, as it does in *Lycopodium* and *Psilotum* ; or it also may be corrugated, following the xylem, as in *Asterochlaena.* This inconstancy of behaviour of the endodermis will be seen again elsewhere, and will be discussed later.

The petiolar meristele of the Zygopterideæ takes a different course of elaboration from the stele of the stem. Comparison suggests that it started from a flattened strap, giving an ellipsoid outline in transverse section, with protoxylem-groups at the poles of the ellipse (Fig. 25, 6). The poles first became distended, giving the characteristic dumb-bell shape to the section known as Clepsydroid : and this is usually of small size (Fig. 25, 7). Sometimes the poles may be further enlarged giving off secondary traces to the pinnae (Fig. 25, 8, 10, 11). But in the largest, as also in some of moderate size, the meristele is moulded into the ' double-anchor ' type, forming by means of its four ' antennae ' an almost complete cylinder (Fig. 25, 9). Nevertheless in all of these forms the xylic tract maintains its continuity throughout, and except for the included islands of parenchyma in the largest of them it remains purely tracheidal. The complex forms into which the wood is thus moulded give an added surface of exposure of the dead wood to the living tissues in which it is embedded. Since these elaborate forms are characteristic of the larger petioles, it may be held that the moulding is a means of accommodation to increasing size, tending to meet the contingent loss of proportion of surface to bulk which would otherwise follow. In the complexity of their undivided meristeles the Zygopterid Ferns are unique.

In comparing the most elaborate steles of Coenopterid stems with the most elaborate meristeles of their leaves the first impulse may be to consider them as widely distinct : and in mere outline they are so : for instance the stellate stele of *Asterochlaena* shows little likeness to the double-anchor meristele of *A. Westphaliensis* (Fig. 24). But herein lies the strength of the comparison in respect of size : both are among the largest examples respectively of stem and petiole in the family. They have started their evolutionary progress the one from a radial, the other from a more or less dorsiventral source : but both in the fully developed state are roughly cylindrical, and both have had to meet the incidence of the size-factor by increase of their tracheidal surface in relation to their size. Such similarity as they show may probably have been influenced by this cause : but such difference of detail as is apparent may be referred to the difference of starting point. What is impressive is that the result is so far similar as it is seen to be. They may be held as examples of response to the morphoplastic factor of size independently achieved, in plants which have persistently retained the coherence of their woody tracts.

CHAPTER VII

THE FILICALES

OPHIOGLOSSACEÆ, MARATTIACEÆ AND OSMUNDACEÆ

THESE three families of living Ferns, however diverse in detail, may be treated together from the point of view of the size-relation, and its effect on structure. In all of them the conducting tracts are more or less disintegrated as the adult state is reached, in marked contrast to the extinct Coenopterids where they are persistently coherent though moulded. All are very ancient types : the first two have for the most part a leathery texture of the leaves, and soft and distended rather than sclerotic stocks. All those of them that have been examined in the young state possess at first a simple axial protostele delimited by a definite endodermis : but as this passes upwards into the enlarging stem, the endodermis tends to disappear in the Ophioglossaceæ and Marattiaceæ, leaving naked the conducting tracts, which are thus directly exposed to the surrounding tissues. It has been suggested that this peculiar state may be related to the semi-xerophytic habit of these families, with their sappy stocks, leathery leaves, and sluggish fluid-transit. But it would not suffice for plants with delicate leaf-structure, where fluid-transit may need to be rapid. In these as a rule the conducting tracts are strictly delimited by continuous endodermis, as they are in the Osmundaceæ, and in Leptosporangiate Ferns generally (*Ferns*, vol. i, p. 185).

OPHIOGLOSSACEÆ

These Ferns being for the most part small, show less marked relation to size in the structure of their conducting system than do the larger Marattiaceæ, and accordingly they are taken first. In all the three living genera the stem of the sporeling contains a primitive protostele, with a solid tracheidal tract at its base. Peripherally lies phloem and a continuous endodermis. Pith arises with increasing size upwards, by development of parenchyma among the tracheids : it is diffused at first in the central region as a ' mixed pith ' (*Helminthostachys*) : later as the

a   *b*   *c*

FIG. 27.—Origin of the leaf-trace in *Helminthostachys* from the solenoxylic ring (after Lang) : *a*, before the endodermis opens : *b*, the separation of the leaf-trace : *c*, the leaf-trace rounded off, and clepsydroid in form : the stele not yet closed to a complete ring shows the origin of root-traces. In each section the inner endodermis is indicated by a continuous line surrounding the pith.

stele expands the pith appears as a continuous column. In each genus the xylic ring thus formed is interrupted at the departure of each leaf-trace, forming a xylic gap (Fig. 27). In *Helminthostachys* the rhizome is elongated so that the gaps do not overlap, and the stele is solenoxylic : but in *Ophioglossum* overlapping is frequent, giving a dictyoxylic state (*Land Flora*, Fig. 236). The difference is one of length of the internodes.

The constitution of the primary xylem of the sporelings of the family is for the most part purely tracheidal : in *Ophioglossum* and the smaller species of *Botrychium* it may remain so. But in the adult *Helminthostachys*, in addition to the pith, parenchymatous cells are freely intermixed with the primary tracheids : in fact the wood tends to be ' vitalised ' in the larger type. The actual diameter of the stock in an average adult plant of *O. vulgatum* is about 3·0 mm. and of the xylic ring about 1·0 mm. : in the rhizome of *Helminthostachys* the diameters are about twice as great.

Other complications may follow, which have their interest in forms so primitive. The first is an apparent further step towards solenostely. Occasionally in *Botrychium* and in *Helminthostachys* an internal endodermis, but without internal phloem, may appear lining the medullated wood internally (Fig. 27). Actual measurements show that the relation of this to size is irregular. The fact of the appearance of an internal endodermis at all is in strange contrast to the disappearance of the outer endodermis in the adult stems, so frequently seen in the Ophioglossaceæ and Marattiaceæ. The second complication is that cambial increase occurs in many species of *Botrychium*, and particularly in *B. virginianum*, where a zone of secondary wood forms a massive cylinder traversed by medullary rays (Fig. 22, p. 78). Like other secondary wood it is ' vitalised,' living parenchyma of the rays being associated with the dead tracheids. It thus appears that in the stems of the Ophioglossaceæ generally, where the size is small the wood is of the primitive purely tracheidal type : but where a larger size is attained living cells, whether of primary origin or derived from cambium, permeate the wood : thus a greater proportion of living surface to the bulk of the dead tracheids is secured than a continuance of the primitive structure would have given (see *Ferns*, vol. i, Figs. 119, 129, vol. ii, Figs. 351, 354).

The structure of the petioles of the Ophioglossaceæ in relation to size presents an interesting contrast to that of their stems. Their dimensions are relatively large, the diameter sometimes exceeding that of the stem. The leaf-trace, excepting in certain highly specialised species of *Ophioglossum*, arises as a single strand after the manner usual in primitive Ferns. But it soon disintegrates upwards in the enlarging petiole, and in all the larger types a plurality of strands appears in its transverse section. This fact is especially conspicuous in *Helminthostachys*, where the contrast between the concrete solenostele of the rhizome and the highly disintegrated petiolar system is very marked (Fig. 28). The subjoined table will bring out the essential facts :

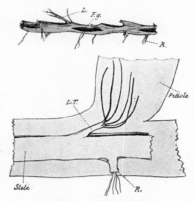

FIG. 28. — *Helminthostachys* : the upper figure represents the vascular skeleton dissected out. *L*=leaf-trace : *R*=root-strand : *F.g.*=foliar gap. The lower figure shows the rhizome-stele giving off a leaf-trace *L.T.*, which breaks up above into numerous petiolar strands. *R*=root-trace. (After Farmer and Freeman.)

TABLE XI

Name.	Diameter of Stem in mm.	Diameter of Stele in mm.	REMARKS.
STEMS { *Helminthostachys*	5·0	2·0	Solenoxylic.
Oph. simplex -	2·5	1·5	Almost typically solenoxylic.
Oph. palmatum -	13·0	3·5	Tuberous : dictyoxylic : 3 meristeles.

	Diameter of Petiole in mm.	Diameter of Ring of Strands.	
PETIOLES { *Helminthostachys*	6·0	3·5	10 strands.
Oph. simplex -	2·5	1·75	14 strands.
Oph. palmatum -	6·5	5·0	16 strands.

O. simplex and *palmatum* were specially selected because of their highly disintegrated traces. They are extreme examples with long petioles. Without any uniform difference of diameter of rhizome and petiole, the table shows in the former part a simple stelar structure with coherent vascular tracts : in the latter highly disintegrated strands. At first sight this may appear to refute a theory that would relate segregation to size. In any case it raises the question why disintegration should appear so uniformly while the stele of the axis remains concrete. Clearly it is not a mere question of size of the part, as it appears in transverse section.

The condition of these petioles appears to offer a parallel to that of the upright shoots of *Selaginella laevigata*, though the parts involved are not of the same category (see Chapter III). In both there is intercalary elongation : Wardlaw's drawings of *S. laevigata* show the diffuse habit and longer internodes of the upright stem, in which the greater stelar disintegration exists. The Ophioglossaceous petioles are very greatly elongated. It may be assumed that intercalary growth makes an intensified local demand for supply of material from the conducting tracts : to meet this a structural adjustment which brings an increased proportion of surface of transit would be specially advantageous, and it is secured by vascular disintegration. This subject will be discussed again later, in relation to the petioles of Leptosporangiate Ferns (Chapter VIII).

The Ophioglossaceæ stand to-day as an imperfectly modernised relic of the Palaeozoic Flora. The prevalence in them of purely tracheidal wood suggests that they have not readily responded to modern conditions. Nevertheless they show in their stems, and more particularly in their petioles, some degree of adjustment in relation to size and physiological demand, comparable to what appears more freely in advanced types.

MARATTIALES

These Ferns are larger than the Adder's Tongues : some of the living species attain great dimensions, with massive but sappy stocks, and leaves of high complexity, as in *Angiopteris* and *Marattia*. Certain large fossil stems of Carboniferous and Permian Age, bearing the generic name of *Psaronius*, are referred to this affinity, though there may be some uncertainty whether the character of their leaves and fructifications will ultimately justify the reference. It may be anticipated that the conducting tissues of such plants would, in the absence of cambial increase, present interesting reactions to the problem of size. On the other hand the question of mechanical stability does not arise in any acute form in the stems of living Marattiaceæ, for some of them have a creeping habit, while those in which the stem is erect are not of great stature : their sappy trunks are massive in proportion to height, while they are covered by persistent fleshy stipules, and further supported by oblique strut-roots, themselves of large size. But in the related fossils the trunks were commonly columnar and upright, while additional mechanical support was yielded by sclerotic tissue, as well as by the densely agglomerated mass of adventitious roots. The dappled appearance of these in polished sections of the fossil stems led to the old name of ' Starling Stones.' The central region of these large stems is traversed by one of the most complicated primary conducting systems known in the whole Kingdom of Plants.

MARATTIACEÆ

The axis of the sporeling of the Marattiaceæ contains a monostele with central xylem more or less concrete, and chiefly or wholly tracheidal. There is a sheath of phloem and a definite but not highly organised endodermis. The leaf-trace for the lowest leaves is a simple strand. Thus the initial stelar system does not differ from that of other Ferns (Fig. 29). Expanding upwards the conically enlarging stem bears successively larger leaves, and the chief feature

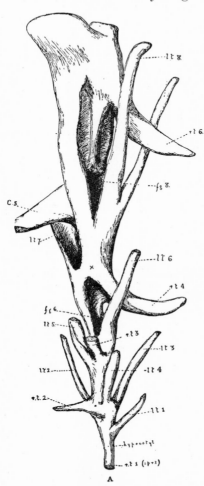

in the increase of the conducting system is the disintegration of the conducting tracts. It may be the fact that traces of secondary increase have been observed : but cambium plays no part in the normal development of the Marattiaceæ. Passing upwards from the base, the axial stele may enter a brief solenostelic phase leading to dictyostely, while the leaf-traces divide into paired strands (*l.-t.* Fig. 29). Presently a vascular commissure traverses the pith linking together the opposite sides of the dictyostele and, pursuing an upward course with fusions at the successive leaf-gaps, it initiates a medullary system that becomes more complex upwards. This progression gives the simple vascular system of *Danæa*, *Archangiopteris*, and *Christensenia*, all relatively small

Fig. 29.—Model of the stelar system of the rhizome of a young sporophyle of *Danæa alata* sm. *l.t* = leaf-traces : *c.s* = commissure : *r.t* = root-traces. (After West.)

types. The initial steps in *Angiopteris* and *Marattia* are similar, though their final state is much more complex. The essential point is, however, that all even the most

complex can be traced to stelar conditions common to
other Ferns : but as their axes expand conically upwards
their primary stelar state is modified in relation to the

TABLE XII

STEMS

Name.	Source.	Mean Diameter of System in mm.	REMARKS.
Danæa Jenmani	Campbell, *Eusp. Ferns*, Fig. 157, A.	1·25	Section shows young dictyostele with 2 meristeles, and origin of internal commissure.
Christensenia æsculifolia	West, *Ann. of Bot.* xxxi, Fig. 14, B.	5·5	An adult specimen: outer ring of 6 meristeles, two of large size were probably in fission, one central.
Danæa Jamaicensis	F.O.B. Jamaica, 1909.	9·0	Outer ring of 6 meristeles : middle ring an irregularly open solenostele : a single central strand.
Danæa Jamaicensis	F.O.B. Jamaica, 1909.	16·0	Outer ring of 15 meristeles : middle ring of 9, two as broad straps : inner ring of two broad straps.
Marattia alata	F.O.B. Jamaica, 1909.	60·0	Outer ring of 10 strands: inner of 6 irregular strands.
Angiopteris evecta	Mettenius, Leipzig, 1863, Fig. 1.	90·0	Four irregular cycles, highly disintegrated : number of strands about 60.
Angiopteris evecta	Mettenius, Leipzig, 1863, Fig. 2. Compare *Ferns*, vol. ii, Fig. 397.	80·0	Four irregular cycles, less highly disintegrated : number of strands about 35.

increase in size, and their petioles follow suit. In fact the
Marattiaceæ carry to extreme dimensions and complexity
the primary stelar plan that is usual in Ferns. The best

published illustration showing the ontogenetic progress of the vascular system in the Marattiaceæ, from a young to an advanced state, relates to *Danæa alata*. It is based upon a model reconstructed by West from serial sections (*Ann. of Bot.* xxxi, Pl. XXI, Fig. 1, A) : the relation of the conical increase of the stem to a high stelar complexity is there graphically shown, starting from a solenostelic state near to the base. A similar relation for the adult stems of the family generally follows from the facts embodied in the above Table (p. 97).

The Table is in the main self-explanatory, excepting the last two sections here analysed, which were taken by Mettenius from the same individual, and they show that with diminishing size, following on a starved condition, the vascular strands are apt to coalesce : in the example quoted their number falls by fusion almost to one half. Thus the relation of their number to size is shown in converse, even in the individual part : a fact that finds its confirmation also elsewhere (see p. 221).

Comparing the petioles of different genera in respect of the relation of size to the number and disposition of the strands, the result appears that while the proportions are not arithmetically exact, there is a substantial parallelism to the results in stems, as shown in Table XIII (p. 99).

It may be concluded from such facts that in the living Marattiaceæ there is a rough though not an exact relation of increasing size of stem or petiole to vascular disintegration. But even in the largest, where the stem and petiole show the highest disintegration (*Angiopteris* and *Marattia*), the vascular tracts of the midribs of the pinnae and pinnules become concrete distally : here ' the crescent of bundles seen in the larger rachis is always completely united, and in section it appears as a single horse-shoe-shaped bundle ' (Campbell, *Eusp. Ferns*, p. 194, Fig. 175, A, Fig. 182, B). In fact the youngest region of the stem and the distal regions of the leaves appear the one to retain and the other to revert to the primitive state. The massive axis and petioles may then be regarded as a distended interlude, in which the structure is so far disintegrated in relation to their large size that the simple original plan is almost obliterated. An interesting parallel is found in the structure of the wood at the base of the stem and that at the leaf-tip, in its relation to living parenchyma. It has

TABLE XIII

PETIOLES

Name.	Source.	Mean Diameter of Petiole in mm.	REMARKS.
Archangiopteris	G.-V. slide 1440.	6·0	8 strands, forming simple horseshoe.
Danœa Jamaicensis	F.O.B. Jamaica, 1909.	6·0	7 strands : outer ring of 6, and one central. From base of plant.
Danœa Jamaicensis	F.O.B. Jamaica, 1909.	9·0	10 strands : outer ring of 9, and one large central. From upper region of same plant.
Macroglossum alidæ	Campbell, *Ann. of Bot.* 1914, Figs. 45, 46.	12·0	23 strands : outer circle of 18.
Marattia cicutæfolia	G.-V. slide, 1791.	27·0	55 strands : three circles of 30, 15, and 10.
Angiopteris evecta	Campbell, *Eusp. Ferns*, Fig. 182, A.	42·0	Over 130 strands : five circles, innermost of 2 strands.

been noted that a richly parenchymatous wood is commonly present in the adult parts : there is, however, considerable want of uniformity even in this. But the wood of the sporeling and also that of the distal pinnules is more purely tracheidal than elsewhere (Campbell, *l.c.* p. 202). Thus not only in point of disintegration, but also of construction of the vascular strands, the basal and distal regions of the adult Marattiaceæ present a relatively

primitive state, which would probably have been functionally incompatible with the present size of the regions
between them.

PSARONIEÆ

In comparing the fossils grouped under the name of
Psaronius with the adult living Marattiaceæ the outstanding features are not only their relatively large size,
but also their complex stelar structure, while in both endodermis is absent. We recognise, however, that the disintegration of the vascular tracts is less advanced in the
fossils than it is in the living forms. In this their structure
may be held as more archaic. In particular it appears that
the leaf-trace in *Psaronius* was more coherent than it is in
the modern forms, originating as a continuous strap. When
we note further that in many, though not in all, there is a
prevalence of purely tracheidal wood, their relatively
primitive state is indicated notwithstanding their high
stelar complexity. There is also a great development of
sclerenchyma, so markedly absent from the living types :
while the massive peripheral zone of roots, which gives
added support, is a feature distinctive of the Psaronieæ.

Naturally attention fixes at once on *P. Renaulti* from
the lower Coal Measures, partly on the ground of its early
occurrence, but particularly because of its solenostelic
structure, which is only interrupted by the exit of the
undivided leaf-trace. Scott remarks (*l.c.* p. 276) that it is
the sole instance at present known of a solenostele in a
Palaeozoic stem. Nevertheless the structure of its root-zone
in all respects agrees with that in the more advanced forms,
and shows its Psaronioid nature. Accordingly it may be
accepted provisionally as a solenostelic *Psaronius*, and
ranked as the most primitive member of the genus. From
this point of view its size-relations acquire a special
interest. The large stem of *P. Renaulti*, seen in section in
Kidston's slide 986, is approximately 50 mm. in mean

diameter : the stele is about 30 mm. in diameter, with a leaf-gap not fully closed. The wood is purely tracheidal : Scott states that in good specimens the phloem is well shown on both sides of the wood, and the protoxylem can be recognised as a number of small groups on the inner edge of the endarch xylem. There can be no doubt of its true solenostelic nature. The large size of the stele may be thought extreme, but it can be very nearly matched by that of so familiar a living Fern as *Cibotium Barometz*, which in an ordinary specimen gives a mean diameter of 27·5 mm. (*Ferns*, vol. i, Fig. 151, A). Thus the most peculiar fact is that this simple structure should be present in a *Psaronius*. When it is remembered that in the living Marattiaceæ a brief solenostelic phase appears early in the sporeling, all that is required further would be the permanence and enlargement of that primitive phase, and that is seen to have occurred in many living Leptosporangiate Ferns. Accordingly we may hold that *P. Renaulti* is an early type which retained permanently the passing phase of solenostely, a view that accords with its purely tracheidal wood. Probably it possessed elongated internodes, and this is indicated by the fact that the leaf-gaps do not overlap.

In most of the Psaronieæ the conducting system is highly polycyclic. The difference between *P. Renaulti* and the polycyclic types is paralleled among living Ferns by the comparison of such related genera as *Dipteris* and *Matonia* (*Ferns*, vol. i, Fig. 180, 2, 3). The former is simply solenostelic the latter polycyclic, while the size is approximately the same. It might then appear at first sight as though mere size does not affect the question. But it has been conclusively shown that the individual origin and elaboration of the medullary system in the genus *Matonia*, as well as in other living Ferns that possess it, have a relation to increasing size, though not in any strict ratio (p. 126) : and the same is found now on comparison of the species of

Psaronius. It will be seen from the subjoined Table that a relation of complexity to size exists in *Psaronius*, though the scale is not arithmetically exact :

TABLE XIV

Name.	Source.	Mean Diameter Stelar System in mm.	REMARKS.
P. Demoulei	Zeiller, Pl. XXIV, Fig. 3.	1·25	Three cycles.
P. Demoulei	Zeiller, Pl. XXIV, Fig. 1.	2·5	Four or five cycles.
P. Ungeri	Hirmer, *Handbuch*, Fig. 675.	30·0	Seven cycles.
P. quadran-gularis	Hirmer, *Handbuch*, Fig. 681.	35·0	Five cycles.
P. infarctus	Hirmer, *Handbuch*, Fig. 679.	64·0	Diagrammatised by Hirmer as twelve cycles in his Fig. 680.

The first two species named above are *Psaronii distichi*, with leaves in two rows : the other two are *Psaronii polystichi*, with leaves whirled or spiral. The disposition of the meristeles naturally varies accordingly, the whorled or spiral being usual in those of the largest size, such as the species last named. In these highly complex axes there are many moot points of detail (see Hirmer, *Handbuch*, pp. 545-565). But these do not materially affect the size-relation. For us the general result is that the most complex stelar state is found in the largest stems, though without any exact numerical relation. On the other hand, from comparison of the living Marattiaceæ it may be concluded for the Marattiales generally, that their stelar structure however complex may be referred to a simple primary source, such as is seen in other and smaller Ferns.

OSMUNDACEÆ

The third family of Ferns of Palaeozoic type represented living to-day is the Osmundaceæ, early examples of which appear with their stem-structure very perfectly preserved from the Permian Period onwards, while leaves bearing sporangia of a type comparable with those of the living genera date back even to Carboniferous time. The strongest evidence of the claim to a Palaeozoic origin for the Osmundaceous type rests upon the structure of the fossil stems and petiolar traces which, though differing in dimensions and in detailed structure in some degree from that of the modern representatives, is sufficiently distinctive to justify the claim of affinity. The family has long been recognised by morphologists as taking an intermediate place between the Coenopterid Ferns and the modern Leptosporangiate type. The structural details bear this out, and in particular the great persistence of the endodermal sheath : for whereas in the Ophioglossaceæ and Marattiaceæ this is obliterated upwards in the individual plant, though present in the younger regions of the shoot, in the Osmundaceæ it is retained with a high degree of completeness throughout the adult plant, as it is also with such pertinacity in the Leptosporangiate Ferns.

The anatomy of the living Osmundaceæ is best understood by comparison with the related fossils : with this end in view the earliest should be considered first. They indicate clearly an origin from some protostelic type such as the Coenopterid Ferns present, where there was a solid core of wood, though this may be differentiated where the size is large. Differentiation is actually present in the Osmundaceous fossil *Thamnopteris* in which, though the cylindrical form of the large protostele is maintained, the wood presents distinct inner and outer zones : but it is still purely tracheidal, without any admixture of parenchyma. Such a palaeozoic type, with its characteristically

Osmundaceous trace and leaf-base, may be accepted as a starting point for the Osmundaceous Family in point of adult vascular structure ; while on the other hand it probably indicates an ultimate Botryopterid origin. A few of the related fossils have been selected as illustrating important steps in the elaboration of their conducting tracts, and they are placed in the Table XV (p. 105) in their stratigraphical sequence. From this it appears that progression in time and in complexity was substantially parallel.[1]

The fourth column of the table gives very briefly the essential steps of progression from a solid but differentiated woody column to a form of dictyostely, as actually illustrated in these fossils. The third column gives the diameter of the stele of each, showing the relation of the changes of structure to size. The first, third, and fourth of the species quoted suggest that a direct progression of size runs parallel with that of complexity of structure, and with horizon of origin. But *O. Dunlopi* provides a wholesome corrective to too ready inference as to the size-relation. The diameter of its xylem is rather smaller than that of *Grammatopteris*, and yet it is medullated. Here as elsewhere the relation of complexity to size is not strictly arithmetical or obligatory : nevertheless the facts as a whole indicate that such a relation exists.

A structural advance thus appears to have been made in the fossil Osmundaceæ from a solid but differentiated tracheidal core to medullation, with a ' mixed pith ' as an intermediate state (*O. Kolbei*). The xylic ring that results becomes irregularly corrugated or fluted on both surfaces,

---

[1] I wish to take this opportunity for correcting an error in the tabular statement regarding the fossil Osmundaceæ, in *Ferns*, vol. ii, p. 141. The names *O. Gibbiana* and *O. Dunlopi* were there transposed. The lines should run thus :

O. Dunlopi. Jurassic. diam. of xylem 5·0 mm. continuous ring of normal tracheae : not dictyoxylic.

O. Gibbiana. Jurassic. diam. of xylem 2·5 mm. to 4·5 mm. : separate xylem strands : dictyoxylic.

TABLE XV

Name.	Source.	Diameter of Stele in mm.	REMARKS.
Thamnopteris schlechtendalii	Kidston Collection, 1280.	13·0	Solid tracheidal core (diam. 11·0 mm) : origin of leaf-traces protostelic : xylem differentiated, inner tract 7·0 mm. diam. Upper Permian of Russia (Kidst. and G.-V. III, Pl. I-III).
Osmundites Dunlopi	Kidston Collection, 2656.	7·0	Xylem - ring uninterrupted by departure of leaf-traces, and pith within : diam. of xylem 5·0 mm. Jurassic of New Zealand (Kidst. G.-V. I, Pl. I-II).
Osmundites Kolbei	Kidston Collection, 1760.	19·0	Stelar structure as in modern Osmundaceæ, particularly *Todea* : *i.e.* xylem-ring interrupted at departure of traces, but stelar ring unbroken. Pith ' mixed ' of parenchyma and tracheids, which occurs occasionally in *Osmunda*. Wealden of Cape Colony (Kidst. and G.-V. IV, Pl. I-II).
Osmundites Carnieri	Kidston Collection, 2342.	35·0	Massive parenchymatous pith : both xylem ring and stelar ring interrupted at departure of leaf-trace, leaving wide leaf-gaps : a form of dictyostely, by which pith and cortex are connected. Horizon uncertain. Sierra Van Villa Rica. Paraguay (Kidst. and G.-V. V, Text— Fig. 3. Pl. XLIV).

and this culminates in its interruption (*O. Kolbei*), and
finally in the interruption also of the stelar ring itself (*O.
Carnieri*) (Fig. 30). This result, which has only been recorded in the largest known Osmundaceous stele, gives in
fact a fully dictyostelic state : but it is arrived at through
a progression quite distinct in detail from that seen so often
in the structural advance of the Leptosporangiate Ferns.
The two are clearly homoplastic responses to the requirements of increasing size. From the point of view of accommodation of surface to bulk in the xylem-tracts these

FIG. 30.—*Osmundites Carnieri* Schuster. Arrangement of meristeles to
form technically a dictyostelic ring. The endodermis is shown by dotted
lines. The cortex is continuous with the pith through numerous open
gaps. (After Kidston and Gwynne-Vaughan.)

changes necessarily tend to make up the loss in proportion
of the former as the size increases. But it is also significant
that the actual disintegration, not only of the xylic ring
but also of the stele itself, appears only in the largest of the
known Osmundaceous stems. On the other hand, the wood
in all of these Ferns is purely tracheidal, a fact which
suggests that such accommodation of surface to bulk is
more important here, than if living parenchyma were

distributed through the xylem, as it so often is elsewhere. These large fossils have in fact accommodated their primitive tracheidal wood imperfectly to the demands of increasing size. This imperfection may well have contributed to their failure to survive to the present day : for all the largest types of the Osmundaceæ are extinct, as are the dendroid Lycopods, in which also purely tracheidal wood was prevalent.

The modern Osmundaceæ appear as relatively small survivors compared with the larger fossil types. The diameter of the adult stele may vary from 2·0 mm. in *Todea Fraseri* to about 5·0 mm. in *T. barbara*, or *Osmunda regalis*. It is surrounded by an unbroken endodermis, which is continuous up the leaf-stalks. The xylic structure of the stele is of the same type as that already initiated in the Mesozoic Age, at which time its highest point had already been attained, though with dimensions far exceeding those of the present day. In living types the numerous strands, more or less completely separate as seen in transverse sections, are united actually into a dictyoxylic cylinder, surrounding a massive pith, and sometimes lined by internal phloem and endodermis (Fig. 31). None of them exhibit full dictyostely, as it is seen in the large *Osmundites Carnieri* : but none attain to nearly so large a size. In all of them a continuous endodermis surrounds the stele completely, as well as each departing leaf-trace, thus forming an unbroken barrier. This holds for the sporeling, and is continued up to the adult state. Such structure is in marked contrast to the Ophioglossaceæ and Marattiaceæ, where endodermis may be absent in the adult. There is thus no communication between pith and cortex in the simple shoot of living Osmundaceæ : but in some species there may be intercommunication where the stem forks, as it does from time to time. Except for this the pith, which itself possesses an intercellular ventilating system, is completely self-contained. In the large stele of *O. Carnieri*, however, this difficulty had been overcome by breaking down the barrier, and assuming full dictyostely, pith and cortex being thus connected. But the barrier still remains in all living species, where doubtless owing to their smaller size the physiological difficulty would be less insistent. We thus see in the living Osmundaceæ an imperfectly adapted

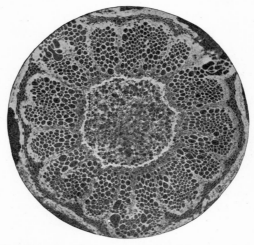

FIG. 31.—Stele of a full-grown stem of *Osmunda cinnamomea*, from a photograph by Gwynne-Vaughan. (× 25.) The stele is dictyoxylic, and an internal endodermis is present.

Palaeozoic type, retaining its purely tracheidal wood, though this is modified in form by medullation and partial disintegration in a manner which gives an increased proportion of presentation-surface to bulk : but there seems to have been no further adaptation than this in relation to size in the Osmundaceæ which survive to the present day.

CONCLUSION

These three ancient Families of living Ferns perpetuate their several palaeozoic types to the present day, and they all share the common feature of conical increase of the individual shoot upwards. Except for isolated instances, which never appear to have been developed with full effect, cambial thickening is absent. Accordingly the same problem has faced each family, viz., that of maintaining a due proportion of surface of contact of the dead tracheal elements to living cells as the bulk of the conducting tracts increases. Each has solved its problem in its own way, with characteristic results above described for their adult stocks. But there is an underlying similarity in their methods, involving structural changes similar to those already recognised elsewhere : viz. (i) medullation, (ii) vitalisation of the wood by parenchyma diffused through it, and (iii) various degrees of moulding and disintegration of the xylic tracts. These changes are here accompanied by changes in outline and even in the existence of the endodermal sheath. In the Ophioglosseæ and Marattiaceæ the endodermis fades out upwards, and is often absent in the adult stock and leaves. In the Osmundaceæ, however, it is pertinaciously retained as a complete sheath to the conducting system : but in the largest of the fossils it is so applied round separate portions of the disintegrated stele as to lead to a state that is technically one of dictyostely. In fact the Osmundaceæ are in these structural characters the legitimate fore-runners of the Leptosporangiate Ferns.

Beneath all these changes, however, there is in these ancient stocks a persistent tendency to retain the primitive type of wood, which is purely tracheidal. This is constant for *Ophioglossum*, though it is departed from in *Botrychium*, particularly where there is a secondary zone : as well as in the large rhizome of *Helminthostachys*. It is retained in some species of *Psaronius*, but in others a diffused parenchyma appears : and this may also be found in the adult stocks and petioles of the living Marattiaceæ, though in their sporelings and in the distal regions of their leaves the primitive purely tracheidal wood is present. On the other hand, in the Osmundaceæ both fossil and modern the wood itself, though disintegrated in more or less degree, still consists of purely tracheidal masses.

The origin of a massive parenchymatous pith within the tracheidal core of an enlarged protostele is particularly well illustrated in the Osmundaceæ, though the method is the same as that of the smaller Ophioglossaceæ. It presents a clear parallel with what may be seen in the dendroid Lycopodiales, and even in- the minute cone of *Selaginella spinosa*. The progression has been explicitly stated for the Osmundaceæ by Kidston and Gwynne-Vaughan (*Fossil Osmundaceæ*, Part IV, p. 467). Three distinct steps may be seen illustrated in *Thamnopteris*, *Osmundites Kolbei*, and *O. Carnieri*, as suggested by Table XV. These steps are carried out in stocks that are progressive in size, though it would not be wise to insist upon any strict arithmetical sequence. They appear also to have been successive in geological sequence. From the point of view of vitalisation the massive origin of a central column of pith would be less effective physiologically than a general permeation of the tracheidal tracts by living parenchyma, a method that is seen in the larger Ophioglossaceæ, such as *Helminthostachys* and in *Ophioglossum virginianum* : in some Psaronieæ, and particularly in the modern Marattiaceæ.

The structural changes which thus appear in the adult stocks of these three ancient families of Ferns all involve an increasing disintegration of the original xylic tracts, a change that may be contrasted with the retention of coherent masses in the Coenopterid Ferns. They necessarily lead to an increase in the proportion of presentation-surface of the tracheal tissue beyond that which would have been the result if the enlarged adult had been merely the magnified image of the juvenile shoot. Accordingly, from the point of view entertained in the preceding chapters for other primitive vascular plants, the structural advances may be held as adaptive methods of maintaining a viable proportion of surface to bulk of the dead elements facing upon living cells, as the individual increases upwards.

The most successful of these three families, as measured by the size of their living representatives, are the Marattiaceæ. It is significant that it is in them that the ' vitalisation ' of the primary xylic masses has been most effectively carried out. On the other hand, those of them which have increased most in size while retaining their primitive masses of purely tracheidal wood, as is the case in most of the Psaronieæ, have failed to survive, and appear only as fossils. In this they compare with the Coenopterid Ferns, which are all extinct.

CHAPTER VIII

THE FILICALES

LEPTOSPORANGIATE FERNS

THE structural changes in the conducting system seen to accompany increasing size in the ancient stock of the Osmundaceæ form a natural prelude to what appears under like conditions in the Leptosporangiate Ferns. These include all the characteristic Fern-types of more recent periods. Such phyletic relations as may be traced between the Osmundaceæ and the several phyla of later origin have been discussed at length elsewhere (*Ferns*, vol. iii, p. 272). Three great stocks, the Osmundaceæ, Schizæaceæ, and Gleicheniaceæ, all of known antiquity, are held to have been related phyletically each to a large section of the modern Leptosporangiate Ferns. It is believed that these three phyla have remained distinct from Palaeozoic or early Mesozoic Time onwards, and that they have pursued their several evolutionary courses, each apart from the others, throughout the intervening ages to the present day. We should then be prepared to see in such structural similarity as the later Leptosporangiate Ferns show evidence of parallel development, or homoplasy. This would apply particularly to those adjustments of vascular structure to individual increase in size, which every Fern must needs pass through as it progresses from the juvenile to the adult state. Hence such similarity as that structure presents in the various types would not necessarily imply relationship, but rather homoplastic adaptation to similar functional requirements. It is well to state these views explicitly before entering on ground which has often been discussed comparatively from a less elastic and rational point of view.

In all the Leptosporangiate Ferns the stem of the sporeling contains a small protostele with a xylic core, purely
tracheidal or sometimes permeated by parenchyma.   This
is surrounded by exiguous phloem, a pericycle, and a complete endodermal sheath.   Where a leaf-trace is given off
it also is surrounded by a complete endodermal sheath,
and its departure is carried out without any opening being
made to the cortex (Fig. 32).   The stem is minute at its
base : each successive leaf is normally larger than its pre-
decessors, and the axis together with its conducting tract

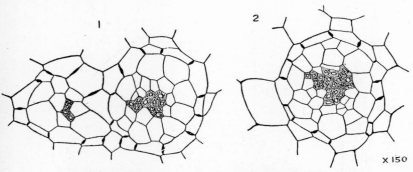

FIG. 32.—Transverse sections from the stem of a young plant of *Anemia
phyllitidis*.   In (1) the young protostele has just given off a leaf-trace, but
without interruption of the endodermis.   (2) Shows the protostele rather
higher up, with purely tracheidal wood.

enlarges conically upwards.   Consequently problems de-
pending on the proportion of surface to bulk, whether of
the stem or of the leaf, will be progressively changing
from below upwards.

It has been seen elsewhere that sometimes intra-stelar
changes in the outline or structure of the tracheidal tissue
in relation to size may be effected without change in the
outline of the stele, as indicated by the endodermis : for
instance in *Lycopodium* this is so ; but in many species of
Selaginella the stelar outline may also be involved, and the
result be polystely.   In the Leptosporangiate Ferns the
xylic and the stelar surfaces react more consistently parallel
to one another in relation to size than in any other large

H

group of plants. The result is seen in those complicated stelar types which appear in the stems and leaves of the more advanced Ferns, wherever the size is great.

PROTOSTELY

In the Leptosporangiate Ferns the protostelic state is characteristic of the sporelings generally (Fig. 32). As a rule it passes quickly over in the enlarging stem into some more complex arrangement : nevertheless the protostele is retained permanently in the adult of certain types, for

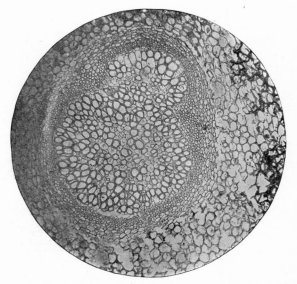

FIG. 33.—Transverse section of a protostele of an adult stem of *Cheiro-pleuria*, showing a leaf-trace being given off from it. (×45.) Parenchyma is present scattered through the central region of the wood.

instance in *Lygodium, Eu-Gleichenia,* and *Cheiropleuria* (Fig. 33) : also in the Hymenophyllaceæ. All of these are relatively primitive Ferns as shown by the fossil record or by comparison : they all have a spore-output beyond what is usual for Leptosporangiate Ferns. They all present in the adult state a xylic core, composed of tracheids and parenchyma : thus they have all departed definitely from that most primitive state, which was probably the original one for vascular plants, viz. the purely tracheidal tract. Even the stele of the sporeling may possess wood of a mixed constitution, as in *Lygodium* (Fig. 34). But in the related genera of *Schizaea* and *Anemia* the wood is in the first

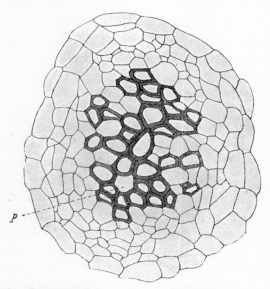

FIG. 34.—Transverse section of stele of a sporeling of *Lygodium japonicum* below the first leaf.   Parenchyma (*p*) is already included in the woody core. After Boodle.   (× 390.)

instance purely tracheidal, which may be regarded as an ancestral state (Fig. 32).

This definite departure from the purely tracheidal wood in living Ferns is in strong contrast to the protostelic structure seen in *Thamnopteris, Lepidodendron, Asteroxylon*, and other ancient but extinct plants.   It suggests that purely tracheidal wood does not possess survival value to-day, except in small strands.   A remedy appears to have been found in the presence of living cells distributed through the primary wood, supplying as it does a vital relation which would otherwise be lacking.   Modern wood

is thus habitually ' vitalised.' (See Fig. 37, p. 122.) When
living cells are associated with the tracheids there appears
to be no limit to the size of the woody core, except that
which may be imposed by the apical cone from which it
originates. Most protosteles of living Ferns are, however,
of limited dimensions : for instance, in adult specimens of
Lygodium or *Cheiropleuria* the xylic core ranges between
·7· mm. and 1·0 mm. in diameter. Even the very large
Gleichenia Montaguei from New Caledonia—of which sections
were kindly supplied by Prof. Compton—the rhizome which
is some 14 mm. in diameter contains a protostele with a
xylic core only 3·0 mm. in diameter. This is the largest
protostele of any known Fern now living, and probably
of any living vascular plant. But provided the wood be
permeated by living cells (as that of *G. Montaguei* is), and
the apical meristem be equal to the demand, there is no
reason why still larger protosteles than this should not
exist. In the past they certainly have : an extreme example is seen in *Sutcliffia insignis*, Scott, in which the
mean diameter of the largest stele recorded was over
3·0 cm. This has no parallel among living plants, but
it offers no obstacle to the views here expressed : for in
Sutcliffia the wood is very thoroughly vitalised. The
nearest living analogy to the enormous primary stele
of *Sutcliffia* is found in the diffuse primary structure
seen in the large Monocotyledons, a comparison which
will be discussed in Chapter IX, where *Sutcliffia* will also
be considered in detail.

Such living Ferns as are protostelic may, from the aspect
of ontogeny, be held to have retained the sporeling structure
in their adult state. They are often small (Hymenophyllaceæ), and are usually rhizomatous, bearing wiry petioles
with a small area of insertion, while the cortex of both is
commonly sclerotic, with little storage parenchyma. In
fact the rhizome, after the first conical enlargement, settles
down to a permanently cylindrical form, serving chiefly

as a base connecting the isolated leaves with the roots that
supply them. Where such Ferns attain large size, as in
Gleichenia and *Lygodium*, the leaves are often endowed
with indefinite apical growth. In all such types a small
cylindrical rhizome would suffice : but it lacks storage space,
and so is best fitted for Ferns which are not deciduous.

SOLENOSTELY

Where the stem grows bulky, and particularly where
there is storage, an alternative to mere enlargement of the
solid protostele is found in altering its form : this is what is
seen generally in Leptosporangiate Ferns. It appears from
the prevalence of such changes that mere permeation of
the xylem by living parenchyma does not suffice for meeting
all the demands of increasing size. Local interchange
between the conducting tracts and the surrounding tissue
will demand a due proportion of presentation-surface.
Certainly it is the fact that the elaborate moulding which
the stelar masses take—connoted by solenostely and its
further derivatives known as dictyostely, polycycly, and
perforation—has the effect of tending to uphold the
proportion of surface to bulk, not only of the wood but
also of the whole stelar system.

The earliest structural step towards solenostely that
appears, whether in the individual or the race, is medullation : as a rule this passes over quickly to full solenostely,
the stele taking the form of a hollow cylinder, presenting a
ring in transverse section (Fig. 35). Here the xylic ring
is invested on either side by phloem, and finally by endodermis within and without, while the ring surrounds a
central core of parenchymatous pith, often of considerable
bulk. The detail of the change may vary in different types
of Ferns, but a uniform feature is that the endodermal
sheath is unbroken in the process. The change is not
dependent necessarily upon the influence of large appen-

dicular organs, as is shown by its presence in the micro-phyllous *Selaginella*, and even in the leafless tubers of *Nephrolepis*. It is to be approached as a phenomenon of adaptive elaboration of a primary stelar tract, and it will be seen that it bears a general, though not an exact numerical relation to size. This relation may be traced first in the individual life, and the figures included in Table XVI give the measurements of mean diameter of the stele of individual specimens of certain Ferns, as seen in successive transverse sections through their basal regions, where the solenostely is first established.

TABLE XVI

Showing the ontogenetic relation of solenostely to size, as indicated by its first appearance in the individual.

Name.	Source.	Diameter of Stele in mm.	REMARKS.
Loxsoma Cunning-hami. R. Br.	Thompson *Trans. R. S.* *E.* vol. lii, 28. { Fig. 34. { Fig. 38. { Fig. 43.	·4 ·8 1·7	Protostelic. Lindsaya-stage with internal phloem. Solenostelic.
Gleichenia pectinata. Pr.	Thompson, *Trans. R. S.* *E.* vol. lii, 28 { Fig. 25. { Fig. 27. { Fig. 30.	·85 1·0 1·5	Protostelic. Central pith. Solenostelic.

The two Ferns chosen are of quite distinct affinity. They both present a rather long conical region of transition in the sporeling-stem : and as the leaves are distant from one another, the internodes give a stelar structure almost un-disturbed by insertion of the leaf-traces. It will be seen that the progression of structure in relation to size is of the same order in both of these examples, though the figures do not exactly coincide.

There is a degree of apparent uniformity in these examples which is not maintained with exactitude elsewhere. A wide range of variability has been disclosed within the

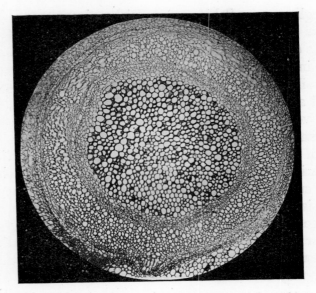

FIG. 35.—Transverse section of the central region of a rhizome of *Odontosoria retusa*, showing peripherally the ring-like solenostele with inner and outer phloem and endodermis, and large central pith.   G. V. Coll. Slide 979.

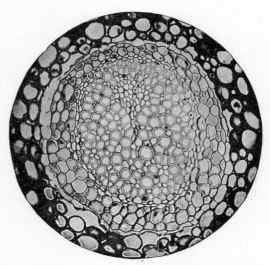

FIG. 36.—Transverse section of a stele of *Lindsaya linearis* Swartz, showing the characteristic structure with phloem included in the otherwise solid tract of xylem.   G. V. Coll. Slide 992.   (× 125.)

Ophioglossaceæ, Schizæaceæ, Dicksoniaceæ, and Pterideæ as to the incidence of solenostely in relation to size. On the other hand, in *Schizaea dichotoma*, as also in *Platyzoma*, in both of which Prof. McL. Thompson has recorded in detail a fluctuating solenostelic state, the measurements varied around 1·0 mm. as a mean for both (*Trans. R. S. Edin.* vol. lii, Pl. I, II, also Text, Fig. 2, p. 586). These last examples point definitely towards a diameter of the stele of 1·0 mm. as critical for them. The result of all such comparisons is to show that while there is a definite relation of the successive steps in the normal ontogeny, there is no fixed size-relation for the incidence of solenostely in Ferns at large. Nevertheless in certain well analysed examples a stelar diameter of 1·0 mm. appears to be a critical size ; in others such a critical point may be much smaller, though occasionally it is larger.

Another line of comparison which throws additional light upon the relation of solenostely to size is based upon the dimensions in the adult stems of Ferns belonging to the *Lindsaya* affinity, where the stelar state has acquired systematic value. The genus *Lindsaya* possesses a type of stele first described by Tansley and Lulham (*Ann. of Bot.* xvi, 157). It is characterised by a continuous strand of phloem which runs internally close to the dorsal surface of the otherwise solid xylem (Fig. 36). But the genus *Odontosoria*, which has often been confused on the one hand with *Lindsaya* and on the other with *Davallia*, is solenostelic (Fig. 35). A comparison as to the size-relation should then be of special value here : the results are embodied in the subjoined Table XVII (p. 121).

All the species of *Lindsaya* that are included have a stelar diameter of less than 1·0 mm. and they all have the *Lindsaya* type of stele : this is general for the genus (see *Ann. of Bot.* xxxiii, p. 13). The species of *Odontosoria* have adult steles considerably over 1·0 mm. in diameter, and are solenostelic. Such figures indicate that the anatomical distinction between *Lindsaya* and *Odontosoria* is related to size. The former genus comprises as a rule relatively small Ferns with stelar dimensions below the critical limit of 1·0 mm. in diameter : the latter are Ferns of larger size having full solenostely. The result of this comparison is to show that for the incidence of solenostely the critical size of stele is here approximately the same as that found in the sporelings quoted in Table XVI : viz. about 1·0 mm. in diameter.

TABLE XVII

Name.	Source.	Stele Diameter in mm.	REMARKS.
Lindsaya linearis	G.-V. slide, 992.	·4	Internal phloem (*Lindsaya* type).
L. clavata	*Ferns*, iii, Fig. 600, *bis* I.	·5	Internal phloem (*Lindsaya* type).
L. trapeziformis	*Ferns*, iii, Fig. 600, *bis* II.	·9	Internal phloem (*Lindsaya* type).
Odontosoria aculeata	*Ferns*, iii, Fig. 600, *bis* III.	1·8	Solenostelic : small central pith.
O. fumarioides	*Ferns*, iii, Fig. 600, *bis* IV.	2·2	Solenostelic : pith larger.
O. retusa	*Ferns*, iii, Fig. 600, *bis* V.	3·0	Solenostele still larger.

The simple solenostele once established may attain large dimensions in some Ferns, such as *Metaxya* and *Lophosoria* (Fig. 44, 1). An extreme example is seen in *Cibotium Barometz*, in which the mean diameter may be as much as 27·5 mm. with a massive pith of only slightly less diameter : this is approximately a similar size to that found in *Psaronius Renaulti* (see Chapter VII). Sometimes the proportion of surface-exposure of the woody tract to its bulk is further enhanced by thinning it out to a single layer of tracheids, so that each necessarily abuts on both sides upon living cells. Where the band of wood is broader, parenchymatous cells are as a rule so distributed through the woody ring that each tracheid faces upon living cells, often with a considerable proportion of its surface. Thus fully ' vitalised ' the primary wood can safely be disposed in considerable masses (Fig. 37).

But it is not only the presentation-surface of the wood that is affected by changes of form of the conducting tract. There is also the endodermis, which is itself a limiting and

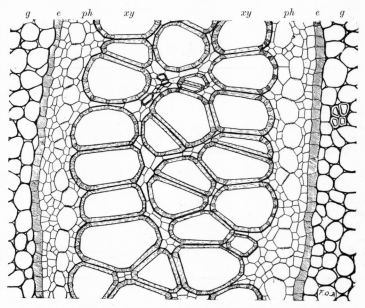

FIG. 37.—Part of a transverse section of a meristele of the Bracken. g=ground parenchyma : e=endodermis : ph=phloem : xy=xylem, consisting of large tracheids with parenchyma interspersed. Here every tracheid faces upon living cells. (×75.)
        This section is here introduced as an example of effective vitalisation, though the stelar state is itself highly elaborated.

controlling surface of transit. In the elaborations of sole-nostely, and particularly in the still higher segregation seen in advanced Leptosporangiate Ferns, this layer is also involved. It will lie with physiologists to determine the relative functional importance to be attached to these two surfaces, distinct as they are both structurally and function-ally. An analogy may be pointed out with a similar question in Algal cells where the chloroplasts are large, as in the Conjugatæ. The surface of the chloroplast and the outer limit of the protoplast that embeds it sometimes react independently to Size : sometimes they run parallel one to another. In this again there is a problem of relative permeability of the two surfaces awaiting the physiologist. He cannot assume that they are identical : indeed the facts suggest that they are not. But the formal facts are what specially interest us here, and in particular the relation of the changes in form, as actually observed in either case, to the area of these two distinct presentation-surfaces (see Chapter XI).

ELABORATIONS OF SOLENOSTELY

The further complications of the primary conducting tract seen in the Leptosporangiate Ferns may be referred in origin to the simple solenostele, and be recognised as elaborations from it ; since they all involve increasing disintegration of the vascular system. As a rule the disintegration is related to increasing size of the individual, or of the type. A necessary consequence is an enhanced surface-exposure of the conducting tracts to the living tissues that surround them above that which mere magnification without change of form would give. The function of the vascular system is not merely conveyance of material between distant points, but also its distribution on the way : and this is specially necessary where storage exists. Hence the importance in such cases of upholding a high proportion of surface to bulk.

Another aspect attending the elaboration of the primary vascular tracts of Leptosporangiate Ferns, which follows on their conical increase upwards, is its effect on the ventilation of tissues. A hollow cylindrical stele, confined by continuous endodermis within and without, will act as a gas-barrier between the ventilating system of the cortex and that of the enclosed pith. It is for physiologists to estimate the effect of this : from the morphological side it is clear that so far as such a barrier is effective, its influence being proportional to its surface, the larger the simple solenostele and the longer the internodes between the leaf-gaps (these being the only channels of direct ventilation), the greater the risk of physiological inefficiency. Thus solenostely, though it tends to uphold the proportion of surface to bulk, will not in itself prove an ideal solution of

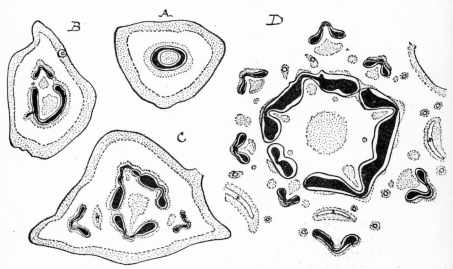

FIG. 38.—Transverse sections of rhizomes of successive ages of *Plagiogyria pycnophylla*, showing transition from solenostely to dictyostely. A, soleno-stelic rhizome : B, same giving off a leaf-trace : C, larger rhizome with two leaf-gaps : D, vascular system of an adult, dictyostelic rhizome : peripheral sclerenchyma omitted. Xylem black, sclerenchyma dotted. (A, B, C × 4 : D × 2.)

all problems of increasing size. Some form of further disintegration would appear advantageous from the point of view of ventilation.

It is believed that some such biological aspect of the high elaboration of the primary tracts seen in the Leptosporangiate Ferns will be more illuminating than any mere comparison of their form, or classification of the types of moulding that they present. Nevertheless it is necessary that the recognised terminology should be preserved, so as to secure an orderly presentment of the facts, and a methodical use of them in comparison with a view to phyletic study.

The simplest elaboration of solenostely is that designated *dictyostely* : it is the natural consequence of crowded leaves and overlapping leaf-gaps, so disposed that the stelar system forms a cylindrical net-work. All intermediate steps can be found between solenostely and dictyostely, and the transition may even be followed in the individual plant, where an elongated solenostelic rhizome terminates in a tuft of closely packed leaves, as in *Plagiogyria* (Fig. 38). The final result seen in the solid is well represented by the vascular skeleton of *Dryopteris* (Fig. 39). The dictyostelic stem is usually distended, and often serves for storage in both cortex and pith. The enlarged proportion of surface of the conducting tract secured by this elaboration of form will be of advantage in the deposit and withdrawal of storage material : moreover free ventilation through the crowded leaf-gaps is established between the cortex and the massive pith. It is then natural that dictyostely in one form or another should be present in the largest types, such as the genus *Dicksonia*. Here the parenchymatous pith may appear

FIG. 39.—Dictyostele of the Male Shield Fern dissected out, showing the overlapping leaf-gaps which allow communication between cortex and pith. (After Reinke.)

as a central column 7·0 cm. or more in diameter, without any vascular supply of its own (*Ferns*, vol. ii, Fig. 533).

Where, however, the pith is large a medullary vascular system is frequently present, which takes the form of more or less definite internal cycles within the original solenostele. This gives the state known as ' *polycycly*.'

A typical example of a medullary system is seen in *Matonia* (Fig. 40) ; but in the related genus *Dipteris*, though its size is larger, the inner system is absent. Thus the occurrence of medullary tracts is optional not obligatory (see Fig. 43,2,3). Two examples may be quoted showing the relation of polycycly to size in the individual plant. In *Thyrsopteris* a runner with a complete solenostele surrounding a column of pith 1·5 mm. in diameter had no medullary strand. Higher up, with a pith-diameter of 2·2 mm., a single median strand was present : while in a larger rhizome with a pith-diameter of 7·0 mm., there was a medullary system forming a second, irregular cycle with again a central strand. A more complete account has been given by Tansley for *Matonia pectinata*, where an adult rhizome 8·0 mm. in diameter may have three concentric vascular rings embedded in parenchyma, each showing typical solenostely. Though these

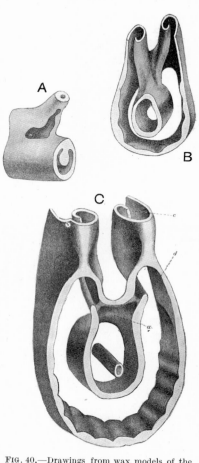

FIG. 40.—Drawings from wax models of the stelar system of *Matonia pectinata*. A, from a young stem showing a node : B, from an older stem, showing a node seen from behind : C, still older node seen from the front. A × 25. B × 12. C × 10. (After Tansley and Lulham.)

run separately through the internodes they are connected near to each node, thus forming a continuous system (Fig. 40. C). The ontogenetic origin of this from a slender

protostele was traced by him : it enlarges upwards, and
when ·2 mm. in diameter it is already solenostelic: enlarging
further a continuous central strand is produced by ingrowth
into the central pith (A), and this then repeats the process,
forming a second ring when the whole is ·8 mm. in diameter
(B): finally a third ring is present where the diameter of the
system has reached 2·3 mm. (C).   In *M. sarmentosa* which
has a rhizome only half the diameter of the adult in *M.
pectinata*, the development stops short, and there is only
a single solenostele with a central medullary strand.   Thus
the facts, both ontogenetic and comparative, indicate that
polycycly is related to increasing size.   This equally
follows from the fundamental observations of Gwynne-
Vaughan on many Pteroid Ferns (*Ann. of Bot.* xvii, p. 703)
and of J. McL. Thompson on *Acrostichum aureum* (*Ferns*,
vol. iii, Figs. 617, 623).   The relation of size to stelar complexity in the course of conical enlargement upwards is
demonstrated with particular clearness by a series of transverse sections of the same stem of *Pteris* (*Litobrochia*)
podophylla Sw., all drawn to the same scale (Fig. 2, p. 9).
These show steps in the increasing stelar elaboration as
the stem enlarges upwards : they culminate in a state of
polycycly in which a fourth cycle is already initiated.   The
similarity of this to what is seen in *Thyrsopteris* and in
Saccoloma is obvious (Fig. 43, 5, 6, p. 131).

The recognition of a size-relation for polycycly at once
suggests that its origin is polyphyletic in the Ferns, systematically so diverse, which show it.   It is not a necessary
consequence of large size : but conical enlargement gives
the opportunity and probably also a demand for medullary complications, which has been seized in such divers
families as the Dennstædtiinæ, Pterideæ, Thyrsopterideæ,
Matoniaceæ, and Cyatheaceæ.   From the point of view of
proportion of surface to bulk in the conducting tract those
Ferns which have established a medullary system tend by
this means to meet, at least, in part, the contingent loss

consequent on increasing size. Presumably an advantage in relation to physiological interchange will lie with them over those in which polycycly is absent.

A further change, which also leads to increased surface-exposure of the conducting tract in organisms of relatively large size, is seen in *Corrugation*. This is only of occasional occurrence : it appears in the simple solenostele of *Histiopteris (Pteris) incisa* (Fig. 41) : in the outermost cycle of *Matonia* : and it is particularly prominent, combined with dictyostely, in large stems of *Dicksonia*, in which it may be held as a set off against the absence of a medullary system

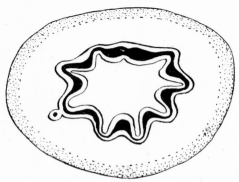

FIG. 41.—*Histiopteris incisa.* Transverse section of internode of a rhizome (× 10), showing corrugation of the solenostele (Gwynne-Vaughan collection, slide 1163, by Tansley).

such as is present in the Cyatheoid Ferns (see *Ferns*, vol. ii, Fig. 533). It will probably be suggested that the importance of such a structure as is seen in *Dicksonia*, where the meristeles are closely accompanied by bands of sclerenchyma, is in relation to mechanical strength ; and doubtless this is so, though the mechanical resistance of the vitalised wood itself cannot be great. But it certainly gives greatly increased surface-area to the vascular system, and particularly to the xylem. Corrugation is also a marked feature in large petioles, in which it will be described later (pp. 135-7). Its effect on surface-presentment is comparable to that of stellation as seen in *Asterochlaena* : but so far as increase of surface is concerned, it is doubly advantageous in the solenostele, for both outer and inner surfaces are involved.

The more advanced Leptosporangiate Ferns, whether of large size or relatively small, are thus characterised by a higher degree of elaboration of their vascular tracts than those that are more primitive. The smallest, however, form an exception to this. Such types as the simpler Vittarieæ present a protostele in the axis, and an undivided meristele in each petiole. They are believed to be reduced rather than primitive types. The materials for the subjoined table, showing the relation of their stelar structure to size, were supplied by Dr. Williams, who has made a special study of the Family (*Trans. R. S. Edin.* vol. lv, 1927, p. 173).

TABLE XVIII

Name.	Diameter of Stele in mm.	REMARKS.
Anetium citrifolium - -	2·0	Perforated dorsiventral dictyostele.
Antrophyum reticulatum -	1·4	Dorsiventral dictyostele.
Vittaria lineata - - -	1·0	Dorsiventral dictyostele.
Vittaria elongata - -	·8	Medullated protostele, dictyoxylic.
Antrophyum plantagineum	·7	Medullated protostele, solenoxylic.
Monogramme graminea -	·14	Protostele, with curved xylem-mass.
Hecistopteris pumila - -	·05	Protostele with oval xylem-mass.

The figures show a very considerable range of diminishing size, accompanied by progressive simplification of the stele, ending in a minute protostele with a solid woody core. Apart from such extremes, which may be regarded either as arrested or reduced, the rule holds generally that phyletically advanced Ferns show the highest disintegration.

I

This may in part be related to the insertion of leaves, as in ordinary dictyostely : but in addition to this gaps appear in the conducting tracts that are independent in origin, and are styled '*perforations.*' They are present even in upright stocks, such as *Deparia* (*Ferns,* i, Figs. 160, 172) : but they are specially prominent in elongated rhizomes, such as those of *Davallia, Polypodium,* or *Stenochlæna* (Fig. 42). They are particularly numerous in the large stocks of *Platycerium,* where they have the effect of breaking up the complex vascular system into small isolated strands as seen in transverse section (Fig. 43, 7, 8). Each perforation is lined by endodermis, which shuts in the vascular tissue completely. A good example has been worked out in detail in *Gymnogramme japonica* : here the perforations have led to a high degree of disintegration, both in the rhizome and in the petiole (*Ferns,* vol. i, Fig. 160). This goes along with very considerable size of both. From measurements

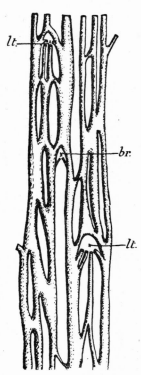

FIG. 42.—*Stenochlæna tenui-folia,* after Mettenius. Stelar system flattened out into a single plane, showing perforations. *lt.*=leaf-trace : *br.*=vascular supply to a branch.

supplied by Prof. McL. Thompson the mean diameter of the rhizome may be about 7·0 mm., and that of the petiole about 3·5 mm.

The frequency in occurrence of perforations in the vascular system of the larger modern types, with their numerous genera and species and their prevalent storage-habit, is evidence of the physiological advantage which this feature brings. By such means the proportion of exposed stelar surface is maintained, while the living cortex is thereby more closely connected with the central pith than it would have been if the stelar sheet were unbroken. It will be shown later that perforations are often present also in petioles, even where they are absent from the stelar system of the stem.

The leafless stolons and tubers of *Nephrolepis* have a special value in this relation, since in them the stele is unaffected by such influence

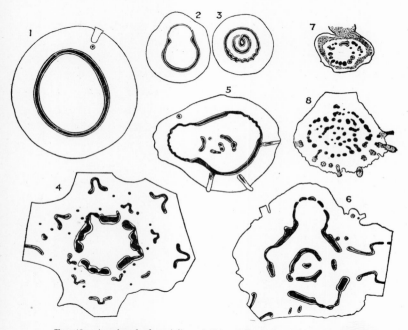

FIG. 43.—A series of solenostelic and dictyostelic stems of Ferns, in transverse section, all drawn to the same scale. (× 2.) 1, *Metaxya* : 2, *Dipteris* : 3, *Matonia* : 4, *Plagiogyria* : 5, *Thyrsopteris* : 6, *Saccoloma* : 7, *Platycerium alcicorne* : 8, *Platycerium æthiopicum*. These drawings show that for Ferns at large the disintegration of the stele does not depend on absolute size alone.

as appendages may exert : its modifications of form will thus be inherent in the stele itself.

The main facts of behaviour of the vascular system are well known through the investigations of Lachmann (*Thesis*, Paris, 1899), Sahni (*New Phyt.* vol. xiv, p. 251 ; vol. xv, p. 72), and others. The stolon is cylindrical, bearing protective dermal scales. It is traversed by a protostele with a solid xylem-core, which is cylindrical also where the size is small, but it is variously fluted where it is larger : in a stolon of *N. volubilis* it is over 2 mm., and the stele about 1 mm. in diameter, and the fluted xylem showed eight projecting protoxylems (Sahni, *l.c.* Pl. IV, Fig. 1). Frequently the stolon expands distally to form a tuber, and the protostele itself expands and disintegrates to form a cylindrical network of meristeles. In a given case the expansion started from a stolon 1·6 mm. in diameter, and the diameter of the tuber reached 11·0 mm. Distally it contracted again to a conical tip, the network of meristeles contracting to reconstruct a protostele with an internal medulla (Fig. 44).

Starting from the base of a certain tuber, Sahni describes how the xylem begins to dilate in a funnel-like manner, and acquires a central mass of phloem which enlarges, and is soon followed successively by pericycle, endodermis, and ground tissue : the result appears as a

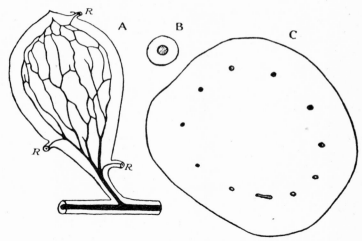

FIG. 44.—*Nephrolepis cordifolia.* A, stolon bearing a tuber, in which the protostele breaks up into a cylindrical network, contracting again at the apex. R=root (after Sahni) : B, transverse section of a protostelic stolon (×5) : C, transverse section of a tuber (×5), showing ring of meristeles each limited by endodermis. Diameter of stolon 1·6 mm. Diameter of tuber 11·0 mm.

typical solenostele. Its mean diameter was ·34 mm., an actual size which ranks slightly above that of the solenosteles of two species of *Dennstœdtia* which have been observed, but smaller than in most solenostelic stems. Thence the stele expands with increasing disintegration, till in the most distended region of the tuber it is represented by a ring of numerous meristeles lying near to the periphery.

(Compare Fig. 44, B, C.) Approaching the apex a converse consolidation is seen, till finally the protostelic state is resumed. The relation of structural detail to size is shown in the subjoined Table, which has been based upon Sahni's drawings (*l.c.* Figs. 2, 3), and on his own slides of *N. cordifolia*, kindly lent for the purpose : the succession is from the base upwards. The lettering (A-D and D-A) is according to his figures above quoted.

TABLE XIX

Designation of Sections.		Mean Diameter of Stele in mm.	REMARKS.
Fig. 2. Basal region	A	·34	Solenostelic.
	B	·40	One separate meristele.
	C	·50	One separate meristele : larger meristele dividing.
	D	·56	One separate meristele : three partial divisions.
Section not drawn by Sahni		·90	Four separate meristeles.
ENLARGED MIDDLE REGION OF TUBER NOT REPRESENTED.			
Section not drawn by Sahni		·90	Two smaller separate meristeles and one larger.
Fig. 3. Apical region	D	·70	Stele united : three separate tracts of xylem.
	C	·67	Stele united : stele quadrangular.
	B	·57	Stele rounding off : open ring of xylem.
	A	·55	Stele rounding off : xylem ring closed.
Section not drawn by Sahni		·35	Stele rounded : xylem solid but ' vitalised.'

Though in the main the apical series of sections shows the converse structural changes to those seen at the base, neither the details of form nor the measurements correspond with accuracy. Nevertheless the one is essentially the converse of the other, both in structure and in size-relation : while both changes are independent of appendicular organs. The conclusion is that the changes whether basal or apical are related to the size of the part.

PETIOLAR MERISTELES

In Chapter VI the origin of the petiolar meristele has been referred comparatively to a simple vascular tract such as is seen in the leaf-trace of *Thamnopteris*. In that early fossil, as well as in the living Osmundaceæ, pro-gressive amplification was secured not by a simple enlarge-ment of the oval meristele, but by widening it out into a channelled strap, with its margins curved inwards, so as to give a horse-shoe outline in transverse section. In place of the single protoxylem a plurality of these appeared (*Ferns*, vol. i, Fig. 155). Such a change in *Thamnopteris* is accom-panied by a very great increase in size : for instance, the greater diameter of one of the outermost leaf-traces of the well-known section of this fossil is about four times that of one of the oval leaf-traces just separated from the central stele (Kidston and G.-V., *Trans. R. S. Edin.* vol. xlvi, Pl. I.; *Ferns*, vol. ii, Fig. 429). A like increase in size appears in transverse sections of the leaf-bases of any modern Osmundaceous Fern (*Ferns*, vol. ii, Fig. 425). The effect of such a widening upwards of the sheet of vascular tissue, completely surrounded as it is by endodermis, will be to impose a structural barrier between the ventilated cortex and the parenchyma within the curved meristele ; and that effect would be greater the larger the size of the petiole which it enters. Notwithstanding this the continuity of the meristele as a channelled strap is habitually maintained in many Leptosporangiate Ferns, which on other grounds are held to be relatively primitive : for instance, the Osmundaceæ, Schizæaceæ, and Gleicheniaceæ, though in the last with their contracted meristeles no acute question would arise. But it is also retained in the adult leaves of others that are held as derivative, such as *Metaxya* with a meristele over 5·0 mm. in diameter, or *Pteris podo-phylla* with a diameter of over 10·0 mm. These may be held as conservative types, which have remained unchanged, notwithstanding any disability which the continuous sheet of their meristele may impose (Fig. 45, 1, 3).

But in others the fully developed meristele is interrupted by one or more perforations, particularly near to the leaf-base. The effect of this in transverse section of the petiole is to present the meristele as divided into two or more parts : these are often very numerous in large leaves. Each is completely surrounded by endodermis, and the parts are disposed, even in complicated examples, according to the usual horse-shoe curve, or some modification of it

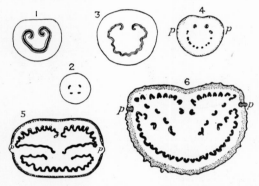

FIG. 45.—Transverse sections of petioles, all drawn to the same scale (× 2). 1, *Dipteris conjugata* : 2, *Dipteris Lobbiana* : 3, *Metaxya* : 4, *Phlebodium aureum* : 5, *Thyrsopteris* : 6, *Alsophila*. These show that while greater size leads to vascular disintegration, there is no definite proportion. *p*, indicates the position of the pneumatophores.

(Fig. 45, 4-6). All such states are probably derivative. Their relation to size suggests an adaptive reading of the morphological facts : there is in fact a rupture of the physiological barrier.

The most familiar example, and the simplest, is that of the type styled by Bertrand and Cornaille the ' Onocleoid,' where a single median perforation divides the meristele into two equal parts (Fig. 46). It may even extend downwards to the stele itself, so that the leaf-trace is binary. Following their course upwards the two straps unite sooner or later in the median plane, giving thus a concrete meristele for the upper region. With some variety of detail this type is characteristic of many Ferns of moderate size, such as *Onoclea, Matteuccia, Asplenium, Athyrium, Scolopendrium, Gymnogramme*, etc. Probably the perforation has had a homoplastic origin. As a further example the genus *Plagiogyria* may be quoted. Here the leaf-trace originates as a gutter-shaped strap traversing the distended leaf-base, which bears two rows of pneumatophores (*Ferns*, i, Fig. 194). In *P. pycnophylla* no interruption of the strap is seen : but in *P. semicordata*, as the meristele traverses the enlarged base and passes the pneumatophores,

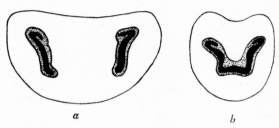

a   *b*

FIG. 46.—Transverse section of petiole of *Athyrium filix fœmina* : *a*, near base : *b*, higher up. After Luerssen. (× 7.)

it segregates into three parts, the perforations between these corresponding to their rows. This fact suggests a functional relation, in allowing gaseous interchange from the outer air through the pneumatophores, and onwards through the perforations of the meristelar sheet.

That this is a real relation is shown more clearly in *Lophosoria*, a Fern of distinct affinity from *Plagiogyria*, and of much larger size. Here also two lateral perforations of the characteristic horse-shoe are seen as it traverses the base of the adult petiole : but they do not appear in the leaves of the sporeling, or of the young runners. The leaf-trace originates as a simple meristele : this soon takes a complicated form with deep involutions, which lie opposite to the longitudinal lines of ventilation that here interrupt the hard rind of the petiole. In leaves of medium size, and in all large leaves, the meristele is perforated along the lines of involution opposite to the pneumatophoric lines (Fig. 47). Passing upwards the three straps thus separated may fuse marginally from time to time : but sooner or later they finally join to form an integral meristele again. In a specific case the final fusion occurred where the petiole was about 7·0 mm. in diameter. Here then perforation is correlated with size, while the interruptions are localised in relation to the lines of ventilation through the sclerotic rind of the petiole.

The relation of the deep lateral involutions of the meristele in Ferns to the ventilating channels has long been

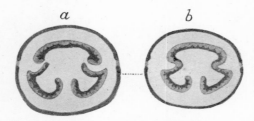

Fig. 47.—Transverse sections of the petiole of *Lophosoria*. *a*, is from a point near the base, and shows the trace divided into three strands, and opposite each perforation is an interruption of the superficial sclerenchyma for purposes of ventilation : *b*, was taken from a point higher up, and the gaps are closed, so that the meristele is continuous. (× 4.)

known : they are deepest in large petioles, such as *Thyrsopteris* or *Alsophila* (Fig. 45, 5, 6). The perforations appear as a rule where these or other corrugations of the meristele are already present. Corrugation itself may be held as a concession to large size, tending as in the stem to level up the proportion of surface to bulk : it is illustrated in the unbroken meristele of *Metaxya* (Fig. 45, 3). In *Thyrsopteris* with a deeply corrugated meristele, the interruptions are again at the base of the deep lateral involutions (5), and opposite to the lateral pneumatophores (*p*). Extreme examples of interruption appear in the Cyatheoid petioles, which may be 4 cm. or more in diameter. The details of these have been so thoroughly examined by Bertrand and Cornaille that a single illustration will suffice (*Études sur la*

structure des Filicinées actuelles, Lille, 1902).   In *Alsophila*
(Fig. 45, 7) the general outline of the highly disintegrated
meristele shows the usual deep involutions opposite
the lateral lines of ventilation.   The disposition of the
numerous isolated portions of it indicates their genetic
relation to an original corrugated meristele.

As bearing on the size-relation of this an interesting
feature is brought out by Ogura, who demonstrates in
many large Ferns a converse closing of the perforations of
the meristele as it is followed upwards, with constantly
diminishing size, towards the leaf-tip (*Japanese Cyatheaceœ*

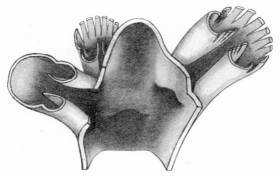

FIG. 48.—Portion of the vascular system of the stem of *Cibotium Baro-metz*, seen from within, and showing the departure of three leaf-traces, which become disintegrated as they pass into the petiole. (After Gwynne-Vaughan.)

Tokyo, 1927, p. 335, Fig. 74).   A striking instance is seen
in *Cibotium Barometz*.   The advancing disintegration of
the meristele of this Fern at the leaf-base has been demonstrated by Gwynne-Vaughan, with a drawing of it in the
solid (Fig. 48).   The disintegrated state is continued upwards through the leaf ; but Ogura has shown a converse
re-integration as the rachis diminishes towards the leaf-tip
(Fig. 49).   Similar facts, which he has demonstrated with
varying detail for many large Ferns, indicate a relation
between size and disintegration of the meristele.   Its
physiological justification probably lies in the perforation
of the otherwise impermeable barrier to ventilation which

a continuous meristelar sheet would offer : naturally its effect would be greatest where the size is large.

The relation between pneumatophores and vascular structure, now recognised for many Fern leaves, is specially critical in those in which the rind is sclerotic, as it is in the dendroid types : it is most marked in the larger Cyatheoids. Here the dictyostele of the stem consists of broad continuous meristeles with massive sclerenchyma on either side of them, which together with the rind will preclude direct ventilation. They give rise at each leaf-gap to a leaf-trace that is highly disintegrated from its very base (*Ferns*, ii, Figs. 559, 560). The sclerotic rind is continuous opposite to these meristeles, or it possesses only occasional ventilation-pits. But at the leaf-base, where the leaf-trace is highly disintegrated, ventilation is afforded by numerous large ventilation-pits (Fig. 50). Thus structurally surface-ventilation and vascular disintegration march together. This is merely an extreme case of what may be seen in other large Ferns : but in particular it accords with the structure of the leaf-base in *Plagiogyria*, where the ' aerophorae ' lie opposite to the perforations of the meristele. Such facts suggest that there is a functional

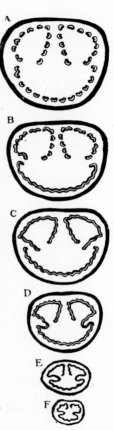

FIG. 49.—Cross sections of six different parts of a rachis of *Cibotium Barometz*, arranged in aeropetal succession, showing the vascular tracts : these are highly disintegrated at the base, but re-integrated as the rachis diminishes upwards. Natural size : after Ogura.

relation between size, ventilation, and disintegration of the conducting tracts.

It may be asked why ventilation and disintegration

should be so marked at the base of large leaves, and not in the stock generally. A reply may be found in the difference in physiological activity between the two parts. The axis of the large Cyatheoids, and upright growing Ferns generally, is a region of storage and of sluggish transit, with very slow apical or intercalary growth : the

petiole, and particularly the leaf-base, is a region of rapid and intensive intercalary growth during the extension of the young leaf. This means rapid metabolism and gaseous interchange, the extension being at first centred near to the leaf-base. It is true that this is a temporary phase, but none the less it has to be met structurally. It has been noted by Hannig that in the adult state the 'ventilating pits' dry up. He remarks that the plant possesses in these pits a peculiar form of pneumathode, which makes active gaseous interchange possible during extension; but later

FIG. 50.—Outer surface of the stem of Hemitelia (Amphicosmia) Walkerœ. The sclerotic sheath of the stem-surface is almost free from ventilation-pits, and below it lie the broad continuous meristeles. But the leaf-bases are crowded with ventilation-pits, and here the meristeles are highly disintegrated. Half the natural size.

when the exposed blade has become photosynthetic, it is superfluous, and the pits are closed like any other wound in the plant (Hannig, *Bot. Zeit.* 1898, p. 9, etc.). The temporary ventilation thus supplied is not restricted to the cortex by a continuous meristelar sheet, such as exists in the sluggish axis : the high degree of disintegration of the meristele at the leaf-bases may be held as co-operating with the channels of rapid gaseous interchange supplied by the ventilation pits in these large Ferns. Their position is at the very point where metabolism will be active, that is at the base of the rapidly extending rachis.

CONCLUSION FOR LEPTOSPORANGIATE FERNS

The structural problem confronting the Leptosporangiate Ferns, as the shoot increases conically upwards, is a peculiar one. In the entire absence of cambial activity the primary conducting tracts of the growing individual must suffice not only for conduction of water and soluble substances through long distances, but also provision must be made by them for the transit of materials to and from the surrounding tissues all along their course. At the same time gaseous interchange between the ventilated tissues must not be unduly impeded. All this falls upon conducting tracts which throughout the sub-class are strictly bounded by a continuous endodermal sheath : and this, while it keeps up a constant and complete protoplasmic control, inevitably forms an obstacle to direct gaseous interchange. Finally, mechanical stability must be maintained. Though most Ferns are lowly organisms some are dendroid : but as a matter of fact, their vascular tissues contribute little to the stability of the plant. No other class of plants has faced such a problem under like restrictions : and yet it has been so successfully solved that over 5000 species of Leptosporangiate Ferns exist, and collectively they form a very appreciable fraction of the current Flora of the Land. It need then be no surprise that their conducting tissues present features that find no parallel elsewhere, excepting in some few Pteridophytes and Flowering Plants : and then only as minor exceptions. A provisional attempt has been made to coordinate their peculiar structure with the conditions imposed, which will vary continually as the individual increases conically upwards : but a more full discussion of the plasticity of the primary conducting tracts of the Leptosporangiate Ferns must be held over till Chapter XI, when the subject will be considered generally for vascular plants at large.

CHAPTER IX

THE SHOOT OF SEED-PLANTS

(1) Enlargement of the Primary Stele

The Pteridophyta present two ways of meeting that demand for increase of the conducting system, which naturally accompanies increase in size of the whole plant. The simpler and more direct is by elaboration of the primary structure, and adoption of those adjustments which become necessary, as the size increases, for maintaining a due proportion of surface to bulk, particularly in the tracheal system. The more complicated and indirect, but at the same time the more efficient method, is by cambial increase and the production of secondary tissues. Sometimes the former alone is adopted, and found sufficient, as in the Leptosporangiate Ferns : frequently both may be combined, taking various shares in the common result, as in certain species of *Lepidodendron*, and in *Sphenophyllum*. In others the secondary developments may so far obtain the upper hand that the primary conducting tracts are correlatively reduced to vestigial proportions, and serve as little more than a skeleton upon which the secondary tissues are superimposed. This is illustrated in the stems of *Calamites*. The series of fossils cited by Scott in his Article on ' The Old Wood and the New ' (*New Phyt.* vol. i, p. 25), illustrates successive steps in the elimination of the former and in the growing ascendancy of the latter. But he specifically states that the sequence he quotes—from *Heterangium* to the Cordaiteæ and Cycads—is not a chronological one, and he makes no claim that they represent any true course of descent. Nevertheless the series presents

in concrete form a transition from a prevalence of primary
or centripetal wood, to its actual extinction : and shows
that it coincided on the whole with the general replacement of Cryptogamic by Phanerogamic characters. It
sketches out an evolutionary drift that was of very general
application.

The Seed-Plants as we see them to-day illustrate two
extremes in respect of their structural adjustments of the
stem to increasing size : viz. that of the Palm-type of
Monocotyledons, which have exploited to its extreme
capacity the primary stelar structure, while cambial growth
is as a rule wholly absent : and that of the dendroid
Gymnosperms and Dicotyledons in which the primary
stele is vestigial, and the conducting tract of the stem is
for all practical purposes of secondary origin. There can
be no question which method is the more efficient : all the
larger trees are built upon secondary growth, and the
trunks so produced serve both mechanically and physiologically to support an indefinitely extending head of
leaves and branches. The Monocotyledons never attain
to the greatest size, while the trunks of the largest Palms
are as a rule unbranched. They have made the best of a
relatively primitive method that is less efficient as measured
by its final results. Nevertheless the Palm stem is a
wonderful mechanism : it is the initial plan of it that is
defective. At best the Monocotyledon is the apotheosis
of an herbaceous type : it does not become in the fullest
sense dendroid.

It has been seen in the individual development of the
Pteridophytes how the axis of the growing sporeling takes
the form of an inverted cone, as the leaves successively
increase in size and in number. In the absence of cambial
thickening this is an inevitable consequence of the accumu-
lating habit. The conical form is often obvious externally
in Pteridophytes ; and similarly in Monocotyledons it is
seen to be so in such familiar examples as Maize and

Pandanus. It is equally shown at the base of the stem of any Palm : if the roots be cleared away, or a median section be taken of the butt, the columnar trunk of a Palm is seen to stand upon a greatly abbreviated and inverted cone. The fact is that in the early years following on the germination of large Palms, just as in smaller Monocotyledons, the stem grows in diameter more than in length, while the leaves successively increase, not only in area of blade but also in the width of the sheathing base, till their full normal size is attained. It is after that period has been passed that growth in diameter eases off, and the stem continues of cylindrical form, with longer internodes, which succeed one another without marked increase in girth. In their several ways the stems of all Monocotyledons are referable to the type of the inverted cone, but it may be modified by adjustment to individual habit. In the absence of cambial thickening their problem of increasing size has to be solved by accommodating the *primary* structure along lines of physiological efficiency, so as to satisfy the demands for mechanical resistance, gaseous interchange, conduction, and storage.

In the lower vascular plants we have seen how, as the size increases, stelar changes have been carried out, so as to meet such needs as these. Starting from the simple purely tracheidal strand, by changes of form of the xylic core and of the stele itself, by vitalising it with intermixed parenchyma, sometimes by the intrusion of phloem, and by other devices, the proportion of the collective surface of living cells to the tracheal elements has been kept up without secondary development. This they have in common with most Monocotyledons. Of all the more primitive plants it is the Medullosean fossil *Sutcliffia* which may best be compared with a large Monocotyledon, so far as stelar enlargement and its vitalisation by intermixed parenchyma are concerned. Morphologically, however, and systematically the two types are far apart. A brief description of the stem of *Sutcliffia* will therefore form a useful introduction to the study of the larger Monocotyledons.

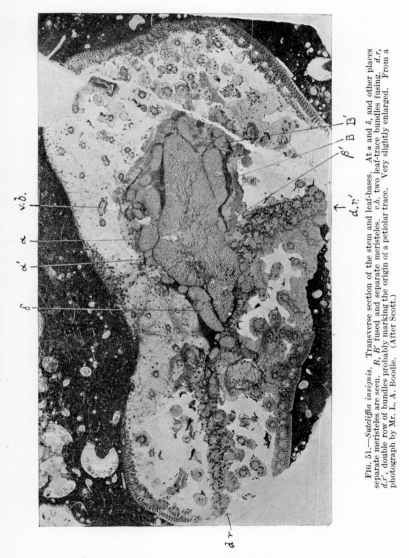

FIG. 51.—*Sutcliffia insignis.* Transverse section of the stem and leaf-bases. At *α* and *δ*, and other places separate meristeles are seen. *B*, *B'* fused and separate meristeles. *v.b.* two leaf-trace bundles fusing. *d.r*, *d.r'*, double row of bundles probably marking the origin of a petiolar trace. Very slightly enlarged. From a photograph by Mr. L. A. Boodle. (After Scott.)

Sutcliffia is peculiar in possessing a single main stele of large size, but there are present also numerous smaller

K

meristeles of similar structure (Fig. 51). The main stele
of the type specimen measures 4·7 cm. by 1·8 cm. and is
roughly triangular in outline : it is probably the largest
primary stele recorded among fossils. It is true that a
trifling secondary growth has been observed, arising from
a peripheral cambium : but it is not constant. It serves,
however, to link *Sutcliffia* structurally with other Medulloseæ, in which a cambial activity takes a more prominent
part. Scott remarks (*Studies*, ii, 201), that *Sutcliffia* has
no parallel among any plants at present known. It is
referred to the Medulloseæ on grounds of general organisation ; but its stem has not deviated far from the monostelic condition, and the main stele forms the dominant
feature of the vascular system. The structure of this stele,
though far inferior in size to the expanded primary steles
of large Palms, presents a special interest for comparison
with these, for it shows how the natural requirements of
large size have been met in a special case that is itself an
extreme one ; but with details differing from theirs.

The stele of *Sutcliffia* is surrounded by a pericycle and a
band of phloem : internally to this lies the protoxylem,
which is peripheral to the large mass of xylem within. The
very wide tracheids that are its chief feature bear multi-
seriate pits in the lateral walls, and are all elongated, none
being of the short type associated with water-storage.
The tracheids are mostly disposed in groups, sometimes
isolated ; and they are embedded in a voluminous grouting
of thin-walled parenchyma. This structure is continued
to the centre, and there is no pith. The interest of this
large coherent mass of primary tissue lies in the fact that
it is fully ' vitalised,' by living parenchyma to which each
tracheid has direct access. So long as the apical meristem
is able to supply a procambial column of sufficient bulk,
it might be thought that there would be no physiological
limit to the size to which such a stele might attain. But
there is one weak point structurally : the conducting

tissues are not ventilated. The polystely of *Sutcliffia* itself appears to suggest that its main stele has approached, or even overstepped the limit of bulk of non-ventilated tissue that is capable of maintaining the vitality required for functional activity : and the type is extinct. It seems not improbable that herein lies the real reason for that apparently unmethodical state of polystely which is shown by the whole Medullosean affinity. These all have relatively large steles, and they are all irregularly polystelic. Their polystely appears to be a structural concession by which a due proportion of surface to bulk of the unventilated, primary conducting tracts is maintained. In fact, that the departure from monostely is of the same order as that seen on a smaller scale in the stems of many advanced Ferns : and that the incidence of the size-factor upon the primary conducting tracts is responsible for the polystely of both. In any case, the fact remains that the proportion of surface to bulk of the conducting tract is upheld by the polystelic subdivision.

The stele in Monocotyledons is not held in by any such functional size-limit as rules in the Medulloseæ : for it is ventilated throughout by intercellular spaces, often very large : while the phloem and xylem are intimately associated in the form of collateral or ' amphivasal ' strands. Moreover the relation of the leaf-traces to the stele is different from that in the Medulloseæ. Each strand takes its individual course inwards, threading its way between those which descend from the upper leaves : thus maintaining a relation between the superficial and central regions of the stele. The consequence is that the Monocotyledons have been able to enlarge their primary stele, without any sub-division, to dimensions far in excess of those seen in any of the Medulloseæ. In fact certain Palms present in its largest known development a monostelic system referable in direct origin to the apical cone.

There is, however, an apparent difficulty of interchange between the stele thus enlarged and the outer tissues and appendages of Monocotyledon stems, which Schwendener had himself felt (*Die Schützscheiden*, 1882, p. 24). He recognised it in relation to the rhizomes of Monocotyledons of moderate size, such as *Convallaria*, where there is a well-developed and continuous endodermis without any passage-cells. He suggested that communication between the stelar tissue and the cortex may be established by the entering leaf-trace-strands. Probably this may also be an essential factor in the construction of all the larger stems of Monocotyledons, though in most of them an actual endodermal barrier does not exist in the adult. On the other hand, the larger they are the more important such communication would become. Their numerous leaf-trace-strands, in their downward course from the petiole, certainly do thread their way inwards through the peripheral tissues, and extend far towards the highly ventilated centre of their stems. It may well be that connected ventilating channels accompany the strands in their course towards the centre of the stem. Hitherto the structural facts appear to be deficient ; it is uncertain whether or not they do actually provide channels, not only for fluids and solutes, but also for gaseous interchange. The existence of such channels as the leaf-traces might thus supply would explain how it is that monostely is functionally possible even in the largest Palms, while in such stems as the extinct *Sutcliffia* a polystelic state has been adopted, though its non-ventilated stele is of much smaller dimensions than theirs.

If the fact be, as comparison suggests, that the oblique course inwards of the leaf-trace-strands through the otherwise impervious outer mass of tissues does serve a ventilating function in the large Monocotyledons, then they might be compared functionally with the medullary rays so constantly present in the secondary zones of cambial origin. But here they would be part of the primary system. A careful examination of young and adult stems of Palms from this point of view is very desirable, and in particular the question of gaseous communication from the outside to the channels that exist in the distended stele requires to be tested experimentally. It is hardly credible that such extended and massive tracts as the inner tissues of the trunks of Palms, themselves containing a ventilating system, should wholly lack communication between this inner system and the outer air.

(2) CAMBIAL THICKENING IN EARLY FOSSILS

The structural complications seen in large Ferns, in certain Medulloseæ, and in the trunks of the large Monocotyledons suggest that increase in size based only upon primary structure becomes more and more difficult the larger the size of the individual. The modifications of structure necessary in such plants so as to maintain functional efficiency, are not only complicated, but they become increasingly unworkable as the size increases. Highly elaborated polycyclic or polystelic schemes, such as are seen in large Ferns, raise new functional problems of their own. Their complexity may serve to meet the immediate demand for levelling up the proportion of surface to bulk in the conducting tracts : but such elaborations could not be continued indefinitely. There is nothing *automatic* in these primary adjustments that would efficiently keep pace with the increasing demand. In point of fact no plant possessing primary development only has attained to the greatest success, as measured by size. Even the Palms have only succeeded, as a rule, in developing an unbranched columnar stem, their constructional scheme not being fitted for supporting an elaborate branch-system of large dimensions, such as the Gymnosperms and Dicotyledons present. As a matter of experience the trunks of the largest land-plants are not based upon primary structure, but upon secondary development through the activity of a cambium.

There is no great class of land plants, excepting the Bryophyta and as far as we know the Psilophytales, which is entirely destitute of cambial activity. Every class of the Pteridophyta has at one time or another developed it in some degree, as have also certain Monocotyledons. But it is in the Gymnosperms and Dicotyledons that cambial thickening became a leading feature, meeting fully the demands of the unlimited scheme of development of the plant-body. It is able *automatically* to follow the continued embryology of the shoot, with its geometrical ratio of increase of appendages. For this no adjustment of primary tissues has ever fully sufficed.

There is reason to believe that secondary meristems have arisen polyphyletically ; not once only, but independently in many evolutionary lines, in response to the demands of increasing size. Nevertheless the results are essentially the same in them all, leading to the production of secondary tissue on a plan that is without limit, and sufficiently ' vitalised ' to be physiologically effective even where the size is very great. It will be unnecessary here to describe the action of the cambium, or its results. Reference may be made to the text-books. The essential feature is that its growth and cell-division may be repeated indefinitely, though it may be intermittent according to season. Thus produced the secondary conducting tracts follow in close relation to the demand made by the growing shoot-system, with its ever increasing outfit of twigs and leaves.

A very constant feature in the secondary conducting tract is the presence of living cells which ' vitalise ' it. It has been seen in the Pteridophyta that in primitive vascular plants the woody tracts first formed, whether in the individual or in the race, consisted of tracheids alone : that subsequently by various means the collective surface

presented by dead tracheal elements has been levelled up
so as to maintain a due proportion of living surface to their
bulk, as the size of the whole tract increases. Somewhat
similar steps, though differing wholly in detail, may be
traced in the tracts of secondary wood, leading to a like
result. A general feature of the secondary tracts is the
presence of medullary rays : and these are present even
in types where the primary wood is most primitive, consisting of a solid tracheidal
core. A brief review of the
facts derived from early fossils,
and leading to more modern
types, will illustrate these
features.

Sphenophyllum, with its solid
core of primary wood composed
entirely of tracheids, may
provide a first example (see
Chapter V). The secondary
wood follows immediately upon
the primary, and consists of
radial rows of pitted tracheids,
with parenchyma intervening
(see Fig. 15, p. 61). In the
ancient *S. insigne* the paren-

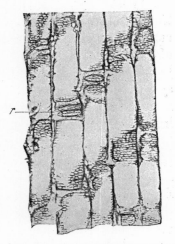

FIG. 52.—*Sphenophyllum plurifoliatum.*
Radial section through part of secondary
wood, showing pitted tracheids and parenchyma (r) × 50. After Scott.

chyma appears as continuous medullary rays, in other
species little groups of thin-walled cells fit into spaces
at the corners of the tracheids : these do not form
continuous rays, but they are connected with one
another across the radial faces of the tracheids (Fig. 52).
This peculiar structure may have been a later modification of the normal ray, or perhaps a primitive character
of the group : in either case the enlarging mass of
secondary wood is thoroughly vitalised, and it stands
in strong contrast to the dead primary tract in which
living cells are absent.

The cambial increase in *Lepidodendron* has already been alluded to in Chapter IV, and the absence of any fixed relation between its occurrence and the size of the part duly noted. Its result may appear as a dense ring of tracheids traversed by medullary rays, surrounding a solid primary column of purely tracheidal wood, as in *Sphenophyllum* : this is seen in *S. petticurense* :—or the primary wood may possess a mixed pith, as in the larger *L. selaginoides* : or it may be fully pithed, as in *L. brevifolium* or *Wunschianum*. There is, however, no contact between the rays and the central parenchyma : many of the rays traverse the zone of secondary tracheids to its contact with the primary core ; but there they stop, and do not form part of a continuous system of living tissue. Their function as living cells is related only to the secondary zone : in fact such stems are imperfectly modernised in their relation to increasing size.

It is otherwise, however, with *Sigillaria*, in which the primary stele is in an advanced state of medullation (see Fig. 14, p. 53). Some species, as for instance *S. scutellata* Brongn., still have a continuous ring of primary wood, and their condition is similar to that of *Lepidodendron*. But in others, as for instance in *S. Menardi*, the primary wood is segregated into separate bundles by parenchymatous rays, which form contact on the one hand with the pith, on the other with the rays of the secondary wood. Thus the condition of these stems as regards vitalisation approximates to that of exogenous seed-plants.

In stems so highly parenchymatous as those of the Calamarians and of the living Equisetales, there is hardly any question of the adequate vitalisation of the tracts of wood, primary or secondary. The structure of their stems is in all essentials the same (Scott, *l.c.* p. 21). But in the Calamarians the cambial activity, which is barely suggested at the nodes in the living types, is continued, and the ring of secondary wood may be massive. It is, as elsewhere, traversed by medullary rays, and though there may be differences of detail in the extent of the individual ray, there can be no doubt of the adequate vitalisation which they afford (Scott, *l.c.* p. 25).

In Ferns cambial activity has never been a prominent feature, though it is suggested sporadically in certain ancient types. The Filicales have met their physiological requirements by elaboration of the primary conducting tracts. Secondary thickening is found, it is true, in certain exceptional cases such as *Ankyropteris* and *Metaclepsydropsis* ; but it is in the living genus *Botrychium* that it is best represented, while the fossil *Botrychioxylon* serves as a probable ancient link (Scott, *l.c.* p. 319). In the type specimen of the latter the primary wood is little more than ·5 mm. in diameter, and possesses a ' mixed pith,' as in other Zygopterids. But the outer zone attains great thickness, being composed of scalariform tracheids arranged in radial rows, with a peripheral cambium and phloem. True medullary rays have not been demonstrated, though protrusions of mixed pith are connected outwards with the traces of leaves and other appendages, thus providing a special form of vitalisation of the woody column. But in the rhizome of *Botrychium virginianum*, with its large medullated stele, the secondary zone is traversed by numerous well defined rays, which are directly continuous with the pith : in fact its structure is comparable with that of a Seed Plant (see Fig. 22, p. 78).

Early seed-plants took a line of cambial thickening similar in general to that of the Pteridophyta. Sometimes their stems contained primary vascular tissues only : but as a rule secondary increase was added by cambium immediately adjoining the primary wood. Where the primary system was of complex form, or was itself polystelic, this naturally led in extreme cases to bizarre results, such as are presented by the Medulloseæ. The simplest examples are found in the Pteridospermeæ, and the complexity bears a rough relation to size.

Heterangium is both an ancient and a relatively simple
type. Its slender stem, which may attain about 2 cm. in
diameter, contained a non-medullated protostele, with its
primary xylem composed of tracheids intermingled with
much parenchyma. Its structure was very like that of a
Gleichenia, the wood being fully vitalised. The average
diameter of the primary xylem, as taken from numerous
sections in the Kidston Collection was rather under 5 mm.
This is considerably larger than that of *Gleichenia Montaguei*, which is the largest living protostelic Fern, with a
stelar diameter measuring about 3 mm. In the primary
state a zone of phloem surrounded the wood. It is between
these tissues that the cambial activity arises, forming
internally a zone of radially arranged wood, which is
traversed by medullary rays, often several cells in width
(Scott, *l.c.* vol. ii, Figs. 5, 6). The secondary zone does not
as a rule attain any great breadth in *Heterangium*. The
chief interest lies in the fact that this plant shows in its
simplest terms a method of secondary increase that under-
lies that of early seed-plants. The stem is still protostelic,
but it is capable of cambial enlargement. The result is
clearly a viable structure, for both the primary and the
secondary wood are fully permeated by a connected system
of living cells, and it is thus fit to increase its dimensions
indefinitely (Fig. 53). In other types of seed-plants, however, the stem is subject to modification according to the
mode of development of the primary tissues : the chief
factors in this being (i) *medullation*, and (ii) *polystely*.

The first of these is illustrated in *Lyginopteris*, where the
primary xylem is highly medullated, and the wood separated into a ring of xylem-strands, 5 to 10 in number,
belonging to the leaf-trace-system. ' When secondary
growth begins, the spaces between the primary xylem-
strands are at once bridged over by the activity of the interfascicular cambium, so that the secondary wood forms a
practically continuous zone, interrupted only by the out-

going leaf-traces. It has, however, a lax structure due to the presence of numerous, often wide medullary rays' (Scott, *l.c.* p. 25). 'The structure of the secondary wood is the same as in *Heterangium* : moreover in good sections a group of primary phloem can be clearly recognised opposite each of the primary xylem-strands.' Scott has followed these strands, and finds that the entire vascular organisation in *Lyginopteris* is comparable to that of the

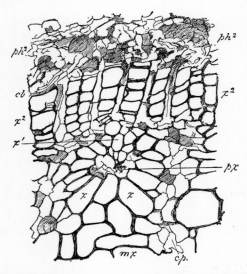

FIG. 53.—*Heterangium Grievii.* Part of a transverse section, from the outer region of the stele, showing a primary xylem-strand and adjacent tissues. px=protoxylem: x=centripetal, x^1=centrifugal primary wood : mx= metaxylem : cp=conjunctive parenchyma : x^2=secondary wood : cb= cambium : ph^2=phloem. (×135.) After Scott.
The chief interest here lies in the fact that the conjunctive parenchyma is continuous with the medullary rays.

higher plants (*l.c.* p. 32). It stands between that of the non-medullated and protostelic *Heterangium*, with its close filical analogies, and the type of construction of a Dicotyledon, with its medullated and disintegrated stelar structure : while in both a cambial activity produces secondary tracts so far vitalised as to provide for indefinite increase.

The second modification, viz. polystely, has led to a structural feature rather widely represented in early fossils, but never developed in modern plants to the point of permanent success : viz. a superposition of cambial activity upon primary Polystely. We have seen that this complex state appears, as a consequence of increase in size : it is a device which secures a levelling up of the proportion of surface to bulk in the enlarging primary tract. It finds its illustration especially in the Leptosporangiate Ferns, among living plants ; but a particularly striking example has been seen in the early fossil, *Sutcliffia*. In the type specimen the very large stem contains a large central stele from which subsidiary meristeles are detached at intervals. In relation to these a secondary cambial growth has been noted in the type-specimen as just beginning. But in a second and smaller specimen discovered later, the primary tracts are relatively small as compared with those of the type, while a larger proportion of the conducting tracts is due to secondary growth ; this was produced from cambial layers surrounding the primary steles of all orders, with the exception of the ultimate leaf-trace-strands. These secondary tracts are traversed by medullary rays, which are directly connected with the primary conjunctive parenchyma : and thus they form with it a continuous living system. The result is a highly complicated stelar state, fully vitalised, and so capable of indefinite secondary growth : the whole is referable to superposition of cambial activity upon a polystelic primary system.

The confused type of structure thus initiated is characteristic of the complicated stems of the Medulloseæ, and of other Pteridosperms. There is no need to pursue the subject into the bizarre details shown in many of these extinct stems. Their disappearance was probably due to the unworkable results thus produced : for the greater the cambial increase superposed upon the individual steles, the greater would be the difficulty of their mutual adjustment to form a coherent structure. Similar instances of the superposition of cambium upon a disintegrated primary system appear also sporadically in the swollen stems of Dicotyledons regarded as abnormal. It has never become the typical structure of any large group of surviving plants, though it has found a permanent home on a small scale in the sappy stems of some Cycads.

The size-relation in such stems will have had its effect on the primary rather than on the secondary development. Here, as in the Filicales the demand for a due proportion of surface to bulk in the conducting tracts will have set its stamp on the primary system, leading to the polystelic state. The cambial development then followed passively as a corollary upon it. That the two are separate and in some degree independent reactions in such stems is indicated by comparison of the type-sections of *Sutcliffia*, which show almost exclusively primary stelar structure, with the specimen discovered later at Dearnley, in which secondary wood is a leading feature (see De Fraine, *Ann. of Bot.* xxvi, 1912, p. 1013).

A comparison of the actual measurements of the stems of Pteridosperms, showing such structure as that described above can hardly be expected to give more than a very general idea of the relation of structure to size. The specimens are for the most part isolated portions of stems : often the relation of the part observed to the whole plant-body is problematical rather than explicit. Even in the typical examples of the best-known genera, such as *Heterangium* and *Lyginopteris*, the structure does not appear to be directly related to size along lines indicated by experience elsewhere. This is shown by analysis of the sections represented by Scott in his Figs. 5, 11, 12, of his *Studies*, vol. ii.

The conclusion from Table XX (p. 158) is that though the structure in each is on the same general plan, the details do not follow any strict relation to size. But, on the other hand, it cannot be assumed that in these plants the structure has no relation to size. If sections taken serially

from the same individual were available this could be
tested. Such opportunities are, however, rare.

TABLE XX

Name.	Source.	Mean Diameter Stem in mm.	Mean Diameter Primary Xylem in mm.	Mean Diameter Secondary Xylem in mm.	REMARKS.
Heter-angium Grievii	Scott, vol. ii, Fig. 5.	14·0	6·5	7·0	Large protostele : pith absent, narrow band of secondary xylem.
Lyginopteris Oldhamia	Scott, vol. ii, Fig. 12.	12·5	2·5	5·25	Stem rather smaller than *H*. Primary xylem medullated, though stele much smaller than in *H*. Broad band of secondary xylem.
Lyginopteris Oldhamia	Scott, vol. ii, Fig. 11.	20·0	7·0	14·0	Stem larger than either of above. Primary xylem medullated, though barely larger than in *H*., and represented by separate Kathodic strands. Broad fans of secondary xylem.

(3) CAMBIAL THICKENING IN GYMNOSPERMS AND DICOTYLEDONS

It has been shown how medullary rays (or physiologically equivalent parenchyma-cells in *Sphenophyllum*) permeate the secondary wood of such early vascular plants as possess cambial thickening. The same holds for the secondary tracts of Gymnosperms and Dicotyledons.

They are from their inception vitalised by the presence of medullary rays, part of which, and frequently the whole, consists of living cells. The rays intervening between the primary bundles are recognised as primary rays, and they extend the whole distance from the periphery of the vascular tract to the pith : others extending only part of that distance are styled secondary rays, and by their successive appearance in the largest spaces intervening between the rays previously formed, they serve to maintain automatically the vitalisation of the whole tract as it enlarges by successive cambial additions. The number of the medullary rays exposed in a cross-section of wood is apparently in about inverse proportion to their size ; but Nordlinger found their number to vary within wide limits in different types of wood. The general result is that living parenchyma permeates the secondary vascular tissues very evenly. Secondary or supplementary rays originate from normal cambial cells, either from segmentation by transverse or longitudinal walls into approximately cubical cells, or from the cutting off of a small lateral cell from a cambium cell by a meniscus-shaped wall, which gives the initial for a new ray, as is well seen in the Conifers. Thus the gaps are filled in as the woody column enlarges. In the great majority of cases the medullary rays consist only of parenchyma. In many woods they collectively constitute the main mass of the parenchymatous tissue which is distributed between the other elements. Exceptions to this purely parenchymatous structure of the rays rarely occur, but instances are found in many Abietineæ and in all investigated species of *Pinus*. Here the rays consist not only of parenchyma but also of pitted tracheids (De Bary, *Comp. Anat.* p. 490).

As a rule the secondary wood of the Palaeozoic Period was purely tracheidal, having no living parenchyma except that of the medullary rays. It has even been stated by Prof. Jeffrey that it was always so, not only in the arboreal

Cryptogams but also in the Pteridospermæ and Cordai-
tales : and that the same holds for the plants of the Trias,
parenchymatous cells appearing as a feature of the secondary wood only in the Jurassic Period, correlated probably
with the origination of distinct annual rings (*Anat. of
Woody Plants*, p. 40). This is probably true as a general
statement : but exceptions have been recorded by Scott
in *Mesoxylon multirame*, and in *Pitys antiqua*, both of
Carboniferous Age and showing parenchymatous cells in
their wood (Scott, *Ann. of Bot.* xxxii, 1918, p. 449, Pl. XIV.
Fig. 25 ; also *Trans. R. S. Edin.* xl, 1902, p. 352). Nevertheless the facts as a whole point to a general progression
in time from the Palaeozoic Period onwards, in the vitalisation of the secondary wood. In the earliest types of it
the parenchyma of the medullary rays sufficed, and the
secondary wood itself was as a rule purely tracheidal, as
was also the primary wood in the earliest vascular plants.
But later, by the sub-division of tracheidal mother-cells
and their retention of vitality, a more intimate relation
was established between the medullary rays on the one
hand, and the dead tracheids on the other.

In the more advanced types of Seed-Plants the wood
itself, exclusive of the medullary rays, may include vessels,
tracheids, fibres, and parenchyma. All of these appear to
have arisen by differentiation from elements of a primitive
tracheidal type. It is significant that in the wood of some
few Dicotyledons only one of these types of element is
present, viz. the tracheid. The parenchymatous system
in these is represented only by the medullary rays, which
are then very numerous. This is found in the wood of
Drimys, and other genera of the Magnoliaceæ, in which
the wood-parenchyma, if present at all, is very scanty.
Such plants are held as representing a very ancient type
of structure (De Bary, *Comp. Anat.* p. 494 ; Solereder, Engl.
Edn. p. 1136). Apart from such rare exceptions as these the
wood of Angiosperms, and also of the Gnetaceæ, shows a

higher degree of adaptive elaboration than that usual in the Gymnosperms : in particular, the close relation of the living wood-parenchyma to the vessels on the one hand, and to the medullary rays on the other, is an index of the high degree of vitalisation of their woody column.

Thus comparison of the conducting tract, and particularly of the xylem in primitive and early types such as the Pteridophyta, with that of early Seed-Plants, and finally with the Angiosperms suggests that progressive steps existed. That whether in the primary tissues or in the secondary wood the initial state was that of purely tracheidal masses : and that by transformation of certain tracheidal mother-cells a differentiation was effected, which has had as one of its results a more perfect vitalisation of the mass. By such steps an approach was made to the state where each dead tracheal element forms contact at one or more points with living cells. On this point Strasburger remarks that, ' in tangential sections through the wood of Conifers it may readily be established that almost every single tracheid forms contact with living cells of the medullary rays ' (*Leitungsbahnen*, p. 30). J. M. Janse reports from investigations specially directed to this question, that tracheids which are not in contact with a medullary ray are very rare (about 1 per cent.) : and that the number of medullary rays which border on one and the same tracheid varies from 1 to 6 (*Jahrb. wiss. Botanik*. Bd. xviii, p. 49).

A conducting column constructed as is that of a Dicotyledon or of a Gymnosperm is thus a living whole : as such it suffices for meeting the requirements of *unlimited* growth. The adjustment of extending efficiency to increasing requirement is *automatic*, whether it be in respect of mechanical strength, of storage space for formative material, or of capacity for water-transit : while ventilation is provided for by the intercellular spaces which traverse the medullary rays. The method of increase by cambial activity is such as will meet each of these needs until the limit of mechanical resistance is reached. Beyond this some change of material, or of the method of its use would be necessary to prevent collapse.

CHAPTER X

ROOTS

WHILE special care has in the past been taken in comparing the details of the primary system of axis and leaf in the lower vascular plants, less notice has been taken of that of the root, so far as general comparison is concerned. And yet in it, as we shall see, features are presented which may well offer the key to a right understanding of certain characters that are in frequent use in the comparison of the vascular system of the shoot. The fact that gives the conducting tract of the root a special value in our present discussion lies in the absence of appendicular organs, other than lateral roots. These are really accessories after the stelar structure of the main root has already been initiated, and their presence does not affect it except as a minor and relatively late disturbance. Accordingly we may see in the stele of the root an opportunity for the study of the relation of size to structure naturally simpler and more likely to yield direct results than in that of the leafy shoot. Particularly is this so in respect of those types of shoot where the leaf is a relatively large, or even a preponderating organ. From this point of view it would be natural to expect that closer analogies of structure with roots would be found in the stem of microphyllous rather than in those of megaphyllous shoots ; and the closest of all should be in leafless rhizomes, such as some of the most primitive vascular plants have been found to present.

This conclusion accords with current views as to the probable evolutionary origin of roots. Comparison of primitive vascular plants, such as the fossil Psilophytales

and the living Psilotales, has led to the confirmed opinion
that underground leafless rhizomes are the source from
which roots have been evolved : in fact, that roots are of
the nature of primitive rhizomes, specialised structurally
for the absorptive function. If this be so, what more
natural than to expect that some degree of analogy should
be traceable between the conducting tracts of leafless
rhizomes and roots. Such are the preliminary ideas from
which we may advance to the study of the primary conducting tract of roots with a view to tracing the relation
of their structure to Size.

Various views have been expressed as to the method of
absorption and transmission of liquid through the superficial tissues to the woody conduits of the root, and its
further conveyance through these. But it will be generally
agreed that the effectiveness of the latter of these processes
depends on the maintenance of a relatively large surface
of contact between the osmotically active living cells and
the dead tracheal elements. In order to obtain a general
insight into this it is not necessary at the moment to assess
the exact proportion of the collective surface-area by which
living cells abut upon the dead tracheids : though that
will doubtless becomes necessary as investigation becomes
more precise. The same rough methods of comparison, by
examination and measurement of transverse sections, will
suffice here as in stems and leaves, to give a general orientation. As in them, so also in roots, a higher degree of disintegration of the primary tracheidal tracts is found to accompany increase of size, with the consequence that the contingent loss of proportion of surface to bulk, which would
follow under the principle of similarity, if the form were
retained but simply enlarged, tends to be made up. The
fact that roots normally yield the necessary supply to the
shoot shows that a viable proportion has been struck in
each individual case. It hardly needs to be stated that
the size-factor involved in this is only one among many

factors that co-operate in leading to the final result of physiological fitness. The structure of any functional root may be regarded as embodying the sum of the effects of them all. But a statement, however rough, of the structural features shown by roots in this relation will serve to indicate the size-factor as one which deserves careful attention : it may indeed prove to have been a dominant factor.

The radial structure of roots, and the variable number of the protoxylem-groups in roots of the same species, are matters of general knowledge. The relation of the number of radial plates to the size of the root was already known by De Bary (*Comp. Anat.* p. 352). A very simple example is seen in the dichotomising root of *Lycopodium annotinum*, as shown by Von Goebel (*Organographie*, III Edn. Fig. 91). Here the shanks are of unequal size : the smaller is diarch, while the larger has a tetrarch xylic tract (Fig. 54). But longer series of sections of roots of different sizes from a given species, each set drawn to

FIG. 54.—*Lycopodium annotinum*. Transverse section of a root above a branching. The larger shank on the right is tetrarch the smaller to the left diarch. After Von Goebel.

the same scale, will help materially in bringing out features of the size-relation which are often missed, owing to the fact that drawings to the same scale have rarely been figured. Such series taken from a Fern (*Danæa*, Fig. 55) a Dicotyledon (*Gunnera*, Fig. 57), and a Monocotyledon (*Colocasia*, Fig. 58), as drawn by Dr. Wardlaw, are embodied here. They demonstrate that the number of xylem-plates is roughly proportional to the diameter of the roots, whether these be Pteridophytes or Flowering Plants.

Taking first the series of roots of *Danæa nodosa*, observed by Dr. Wardlaw, the smallest sporeling roots were monarch, but usually diarch : the largest observed by him had as

many as 20 xylem-plates. Fig. 55, 1-7, shows states intermediate between these extremes. The numerical relation
of the xylem-plates to size, for the specific examples drawn,
is brought out by the following Table.

TABLE XXI

Measurements of Roots of *Danœa nodosa*, taken from Wardlaw,
Fig. 1, *Trans. R. S. Edin.*, 1928.

Number of Figure.	Diameter of Stele in mm.	Description of Xylem.	Approximate Ratio of Diameter to Number of Rays.
1	·136	Diarch : no pith.	·068
2	·182	Triarch.	·060
3	·227	Pentarch : small pith.	·045
4	·373	Hexarch : small pith.	·062
5	·636	Octarch : pith slightly sclerosed.	·079
6	·755	Eleven rays : sclerosed pith.	·068
7	1·317	Sixteen rays : sclerosed pith.	·081

The effect of this in tending to preserve a due proportion
of surface to bulk of the tracheidal tissue is obvious : but
the accommodation to increasing size does not stop at the
mere number of the protoxylems. As the size increases the
tracheids themselves increase in size : the xylem-tracts
cease to form complete contact centrally, and a pith usually
appears. This is parenchymatous in the smaller roots,
but in the larger it is sclerosed, though thin-walled cells
usually intervene between the thickened tissue and the
tracheids. In addition to the increased disintegration,
the outline of the xylem-masses becomes itself less smooth,
and this again tends to keep up the proportion of surface-
exposure. There is, in fact a rough structural parallel
between the outline of the xylem-tracts in these roots
and those of the rhizome of *Psilotum* in relation to size
(compare Fig. 3).

The ratio of diameter to the number of rays will be discussed later, when other examples have been given. It

may suffice here to note such degree of uniformity as the figures show, and to point out the discrepancy which begins to appear in the largest.

The roots of Pteridophyta are as a rule small, though some are large and fleshy. In the vast majority of Ferns

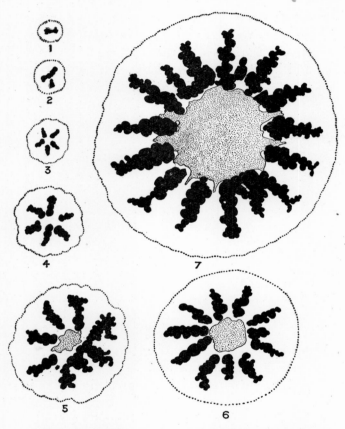

FIG. 55.—*Danæa nodosa.* Series of sections of the stele of different roots, all drawn to the same scale, showing the changes in complexity of the xylem which accompany increase in size. 1 and 2 from sporeling plants : 3 and 4, from young plants : 5 and 6, medium sized roots from adult plants : 7, stele of a very large root. In 5-7 the pith is sclerosed. After Wardlaw. (× 50.)

the wood in the root-stele is diarch, and consists of a coherent plate of tracheids, of which most or often all of the elements abut on living cells. Where 'monarch' structure exists it is usually in roots of very small size, as in *Selaginella* and *Isoetes*, or in the smaller roots of *Lycopodium* : but it is also seen in *Ophioglossum*, and in the Stigmarian rootlets. In all of these the xylem strand is as a rule purely tracheidal : the vitalisation of such small strands does not appear to be essential (Fig. 56). But it is different with certain Ferns where the roots attain relatively large size, and yet stand low in the number of their protoxylems. Examples of this are seen in *Acrostichum aureum*, and in *Blechnum brasiliense*. In the latter, with a

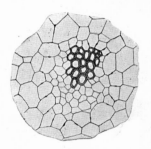

FIG. 56.—*Ophioglossum Bergianum.* Stele of a monarch root, with a solid group of many tracheids. (× 200.)

stelar diameter of ·557 mm. the xylem is still diarch : but it is so fully vitalised by included parenchyma that every tracheid abuts upon many living cells (see Wardlaw, *l.c.* Fig. 8). A root of like size in *Danœa* would probably be hexarch. The included parenchyma in *Blechnum* may be held as a set off to the retention of the diarch type. On the other hand certain Ferns of ancient type are without included parenchyma, even when the roots are relatively large. For instance *Ophioglossum*, and *Osmunda* have purely tracheidal wood in root as well as in stem : the stele of *O. Claytoniana* may measure ·5 mm. in diameter, and still have its xylem diarch and homogeneous. It thus appears that a pure conservatism may still survive in some archaic forms, a structural disability being retained that has not involved extinction. With such exceptions the roots of Pteridophytes bear evidence of adaptibility of their primary conducting tracts in accordance with increase in Size.

In Dicotyledons there is less scope for such adaptation of the primary tracts, owing to the fact that the roots are usually small in the first instance, and the number of protoxylems is consequently small : moreover cambial thickening starts early, making up any initial deficiency. With this at the moment we have no concern, for our question relates to the primary state. Test cases may, however, be found in such roots of Dicotyledons as have a negligible secondary growth, or none at all. The roots of the large and fleshy *Gunnera chilensis* provide a suitable illustration

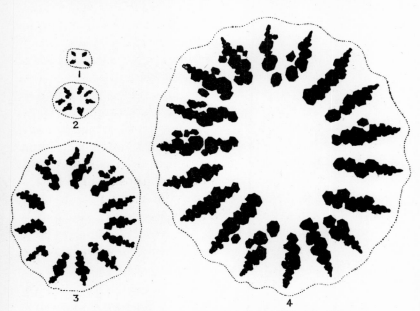

FIG. 57.—*Gunnera chilensis.* Series of sections of steles from roots of small and large size, drawn to the same scale, showing the increase in complexity of the xylem with increase in size. After Wardlaw. (× 35.)

(Fig. 57). The smallest roots examined were tetrarch, having a stele of about ·17 mm. mean diameter : a large root with 18 protoxylem-groups measured about 2·17 mm. in diameter. The interest disclosed by the series of drawings in Fig. 57 is, first, that the complexity of the primary structure progresses roughly in proportion to the size : secondly, that the number of protoxylem-groups disclosed is in roughly the same ratio to size as is seen in other plants so remote in affinity as *Danœa* or *Kaulfussia* on the one hand, or *Nymphaea* or *Colocasia* on the other : and thirdly that, as in these plants, evidence of sculpturing of surface and disintegration of the primary xylem becomes more pronounced as the size increases. All of these changes tend to the maintenance of the proportion of surface of exposure of the woody elements to living tissue.

The absence of cambial thickening in the roots of Monocotyledons has the effect of making general for them what is exceptional in Dicotyledons, viz. the opportunity for demonstrating the size-relation as it affects the primary conducting tract. The distinction is often drawn that in Dicotyledons the number of protoxylems is usually low, while in Monocotyledons it is high. This is, however, based upon the comparison of roots of adult plants. If the thin lateral roots of Monocotyledons or the primary roots of their seedlings be examined, they are commonly found to be based on a scheme of low figures in accordance with their small size. The larger numbers appear in the roots of the adult, and the complexity of these may be held as a set-off against the absence of secondary thickening. The result is that in the roots of certain Monocotyledons the relation of structure of the primary tissues to size can be followed out to dimensions higher than in any other class of plants. The prop-roots of *Pandanus* may be as much as 5 cm. in diameter, and still be based upon primary construction, but with a multitude of protoxylems.

A straightforward example is seen in *Colocasia odorata* (Fig. 58). Small lateral rootlets give a pentarch structure, with concrete xylem-groups surrounding a small central pith (I). In successive examples of larger size the number of xylem-groups increases, the central pith enlarges, and the sculpturing of the woody tracts becomes more elaborated even to the point of isolation of single vessels, or small groups of them, completely surrounded by thin-walled parenchyma (Fig. 58, 3, 4). An extreme type is seen in (Fig. 58, 5), where the 38 protoxylem groups together with their detached vessels occupy the greater part of the stelar cylinder. That high degree of disintegration present in the largest section is in strong contrast to the few concrete groups of the smallest : the natural

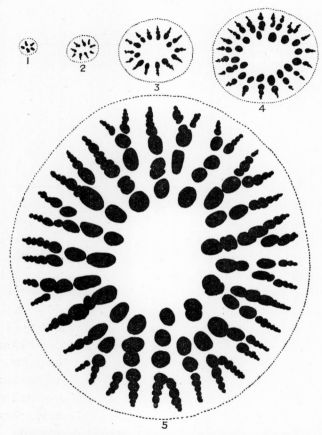

FIG. 58.—*Colocasia odorata* : steles from different roots of small and of large size, all drawn to the same scale, indicating the operation of the Size Factor. After Wardlaw. (× 29.)

result is a levelling up of the contingent loss of proportion of surface to bulk of the tracheal tissue as the size increases. This is a quite general feature in large roots of Monocotyledons, especially in those of succulent texture.

The measurements for the roots of *Colocasia* may be tabulated as follows, the figures being based upon Dr. Wardlaw's illustration, (*l.c.* Fig. 21) reduced to approximately one half : thus the figures in the second column represent the natural size × 14.

TABLE XXII

Number of Section.	Mean Diameter of Stele in mm. (× 14.)	Number of Rays of Xylem.	Approximate Ratio of Measurements to Number of Rays.
1	5	5	1·0
2	8	9	·88
3	19	14	1·35
4	27	21	1·31
5	83	38	2·18

The ratios do not come out so evenly as in some other examples, particularly that of the leafless rhizomes of *Psilotum*, but they show that a reasonable degree of parallelism exists between size and number of rays with, as in other cases, a break away as an out-size is reached.

In most roots of large size the cylindrical form of the stele is maintained : but it is not always so. An interesting exception has been found in the large roots of *Philodendron Adansoni* (Fig. 59). In the smallest root examined the stele was heptarch and cylindrical : and the same form, with advancing disintegration and increasing number of protoxylems, follows in larger sections (1-3). But in still larger steles the cylindrical form is lost, its section becoming first triangular, then fluted, and finally corrugated (4-6). In the largest stele examined, which was about 3·5 mm. in mean diameter, there are over 50 protoxylems, and many large vessels are scattered separately through the pith, while the stele itself shows four deep involutions.

These facts lead on to those which have been recorded for the large strut-roots of certain Palms, where also the cylindrical form of the stele is departed from. The Palm-roots are hard, with a sclerotic cortex, and doubtless they have been developed structurally in relation to mechanical demands, as well as to those of conduction. Nevertheless the changes of stelar form are of the same order as in the roots of *Philodendron*, where mechanical demands would have been negligible. Modifications of structure involving corrugation and disintegration of the conducting tract, and even leading up to polystely, have been seen in the

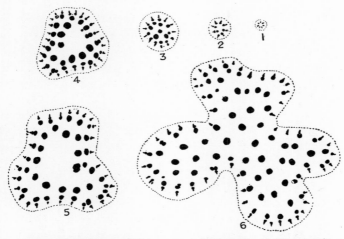

FIG. 59.—*Philodendron Adansoni*: 1-6 sections of steles of different roots drawn to the same scale, showing the effects of increase in size : both xylem and endodermis are affected, the former is progressively disintegrated, the latter showing involution. After Wardlaw. (× 15.)

roots of *Areca, Archontophoenix, Dictyosperma,* and *Ver-schaffeltia,* as they attain a diameter of more than 1·0 cm. At about that size the cylinder is liable to be corrugated : the endodermis is at first continuous, but it tends to dis-ruption at the valley-bottoms : and so continuous air-ways are established between the cortex and the pith. The margins of the fragments of endodermis thus detached draw together, and may be seen at times to fuse : thus closed meristeles may be reconstituted, and a polystelic state established which is structurally comparable with

that in the stems of Leptosporangiate Ferns, though these
are quite different in origin and detailed construction. One
point which both have in common is that the changes
originate in relation to increasing size (Fig. 60). Where
the size is very large indeed, as in the prop-roots of *Verschaffeltia*, the pith is invaded by numerous detached
vascular tracts, which appear scattered through the transverse section, giving an appearance distantly resembling
that of a stem of the Palm-type (Fig. 61). It may further
be noted that with increasing size of the whole root the
cortex becomes proportionately reduced while the stele
expands, as in the stems of Monocotyledons. The subjoined table gives the approximate actual measurements
of certain sections of Palm roots, and of their stelar
tract, together with remarks on the correlated structural
changes.

TABLE XXIII

Name.	Mean Diameter of Root in mm.	Mean Diameter of Stele in mm.	REMARKS.
Areca.			
Fig. 60, 1 -	9·3	6·3	Stele cylindrical.
Fig. 60, 3 -	10·6	8·0	Stele corrugated and parti-ally disrupted :
Fig. 60, 5 -	19·3	14·0	Stele disrupted : one meri-stele cylindrical.
Verschaffeltia -	29·0	25·0	Highly disintegrated vascu-lar system : many meri-steles partially closed, and one a complete cylinder.

That actual size is intimately related to these abnor-
malities in structure is shown by the fact that when a root
which possesses them diminishes progressively the abnor-
mality ceases. As the prop-roots of Palms enter the soil
they frequently diminish thus in girth. Cormack's sections
1-4 were taken from such a root. Starting from (4),

which was farthest from the apex and is the largest, the stele is fluted and even disrupted : there is then a transition

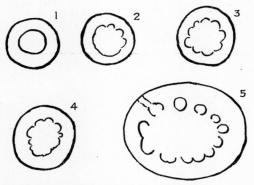

FIG. 60.—Transverse sections of root of *Areca*, drawn to the same scale. 1-4 are from the same root : 1, 15 mm. from the apex : 2, at 77 mm. : 3, at 115 mm. : 4, at 150 mm. : 5, is taken from another larger root. After Cormack. (× 1½.)

from this to the normal monostelic structure on passing by successive sections to the thinner distal region (3, 2, 1).

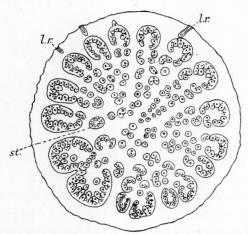

FIG. 61.—Transverse section of a large strut-root of *Verschaffeltia splendida* showing a high state of stelar disintegration. *st*=a completely cylindrical meristele : *lr*=lateral root. After Cormack. (× 2.)

The relation of polystely to progressive diminution of size is clearly shown in the structure of the root of *Orchis maculata,* as it passes from the distended tuberous region. The adjoining Table is based upon an acropetal succession of sections of one of these, prepared by Dr. S. Williams :

TABLE XXIV

Number of Section.	Mean Diameter of Root in mm.	Mean Diameter of Steles in mm.	REMARKS.
1	1·24	·47	3 steles widely apart.
2	·94	·32	3 steles approximate.
3	·9	·3	Single stele deeply 3-lobed.
4	·85	·27	Single stele slightly lobed.
5	·7	·19	Single cylindrical stele.

These figures show how the gradual establishment of a single cylindrical stele follows on the diminishing size of the root, while the actual dimensions are not essentially different from those at which, acroscopically, a like stelar condensation occurs in the tubers of *Nephrolepis* (see pp. 131-3).

Such facts relating to roots as have been embodied in this brief description will help in the estimation of the effect of the size-factor in determining the structure of the primary conducting tracts in the plant as a whole. The most constant fact is that the stelar structure of roots is of the type styled ' radial,' with the protoxylem seated at the extremity of each ray. The number of rays may vary from one to very high figures, and the evidence shows that there is a near relation of their number to the size of the stele, though no exact numerical ratio exists. This is borne out by the table for roots of *Danæa,* and like tables might be drawn up for *Gunnera* and *Colocasia.* The xylem thus appears stellate in transverse section, and where the rays are united laterally it has the actual form of a fluted column, with longitudinal ridges. This structure tends to level up the proportion of surface to bulk of the xylem as the size increases, so as to maintain the collective surface of exposure to living tissues. The natural inference is that the contour of the ribbed column, or of the strands collectively, is adaptive in relation to size.

That the radial structure is not specifically inherent in roots only is shown by comparison with other parts. For instance in the leafless stolons of *Nephrolepis* a similar fluting exists, with a near approximation to the scale seen in the roots of *Danæa*. Sahni's photograph of a section of a stolon shows how in *N. volubilis* an 8-rayed star is presented in a stele approximately 1·0 mm. in diameter (*New Phyt.* Pl. IV, Fig. 1). This would fall in scale between sections 6 and 7 of the series of *Danæa* (Fig. 55) : but the proportion of number of rays to size is rather lower. Similar stellation, though differing in detail, is also seen in stems of microphyllous plants : for instance in *Asteroxylon*, *Selaginella spinosa*, and *Asterochlaena* : also in certain Lycopods, living and fossil. It may thus be present in leafless, or in microphyllous, or even in megaphyllous types, for it is present in *Ankyropteris*. In all of these it may be held as an adaptive state, which secures a levelling up of the proportion of surface to bulk as the actual size increases. Whatever view be taken on this point, an upholding of the surface-exposure is the inevitable result of the adoption of the form observed, and it exists independently of appendicular organs.

It is usually a marked feature in roots that the radially disposed plates of primary xylem are thin, being rarely composed of more than one or two rows of tracheal elements so that each faces directly upon living cells. The increase in number of the plates as the size of the stele increases will also tend to secure this high degree of exposure. Comparison in this respect may be made with the enlarging steles in the stems of *Lycopodium* or of *Selaginella*, as well

M

as with the solenosteles of Ferns, in all of which the xylem-tracts are often no more than one or two layers in thickness. A further step is seen in large roots of Monocotyledons, where vessels often lie isolated or in small groups, completely embedded in living parenchyma : their position shows that they are detached elements of an adjoining xylem-plate. Occasionally, on the other hand, as in the roots of *Acrostichum aureum, Blechnum brasiliense*,[1] and some other Ferns, while the number of the protoxylems remains small, though the stele enlarges to as much as ·5 mm. in diameter, a high proportion of surface-exposure to living cells is secured by the formation of an elaborate xylem-sponge, parenchymatous cells being so freely spread through the mass that each tracheid is in contact with one or more living cells. This finds its parallel in the stele of the stem in *Lycopodium cernuum*. Such examples, while they demonstrate structurally the importance of the relation of the dead tracheal elements to living cells, show also that the methods by which that relation is secured are various, and for the most part common to axes and roots : moreover it is in relation to the increasing size of the part that they come into existence.

On the other hand, in some primitive types purely tracheidal masses of wood are found of relatively large size. This is so in the Ophioglosseæ (Fig. 56), and particularly in the Osmundaceæ, where the xylem in the root is homogeneous, as it is also in the axial stele and in the leaf-trace. In fact all their parts retain this archaic character. These plants are, however, primitive in many other features and are rightly held to be imperfectly modernised representatives of Palæozoic affinity.

Lastly, there remain those departures from the usual form of the stele which are occasionally found in roots of large size. Those which involve only a fluting of the whole stele, as in *Philodendron Adansoni* (Fig. 59), find their corre-

---

[1] (See Wardlaw, *Trans. R. S. Edin.* vol. lvi, p. 34, Figs. 7, 8.)

lative in the stellate stele of the axis of *Ankyropteris* or *Asterochlaena* (Fig. 21), both as regards approximate size and in outline. In *Philodendron* there is no interruption of the endodermis : but in the much larger roots of Palms the endodermis itself opens, and thereby the highly lacunar cortex becomes continuous with the ventilated parenchymatous tissue of the stele. This relation which is only established in roots of very large size (*Verschaffeltia*, about 2·5 cm. in diameter), may be compared in its functional aspect with what is seen in the large dictyostelic stem of *Osmundites Carnieri* (about 3·5 cm. in diameter). This is one further illustration showing how the demands of increasing size may produce like results in parts that are neither identical morphologically, nor systematically related. In fact, *structure is apt to be modified in relation to size independently of systematic relationship, or of morphological category of the parts concerned, and of the presence or absence of appendicular organs.* This is one of the striking conclusions which follow from the study of root-structure in relation to size.

CHAPTER XI

THE PLASTICITY OF FORM AND STRUCTURE IN RELATION TO SIZE

THE development of the individual may appear to suggest that an immediate relation of cause and effect exists as the size increases, and that this works out in such relations of surface to bulk as have been described in the preceding chapters. But within limits the various forms which the conducting tracts, for instance, have adopted appear to be hereditarily fixed : this follows from the fact that within a given circle of affinity smaller species may repeat the structure of the larger, but on a reduced scale. Thus form in relation to size is not directly the outcome of susceptibility to the conditions during individual development. Here as elsewhere inherited structure acts as a break on direct reaction, with the result that no exact scale can be prescribed of structure to size for plants at large. Nevertheless, throughout the evolution of any given race, susceptibility has no doubt existed, and will have had cumulative effect in producing the results which we see. It would then be as a morphoplastic factor, effective not only in the individual life but throughout the evolutionary history, that the condition of Size would impress itself upon present form. This is the view which is here entertained in discussing the plasticity of external form, as well as of internal structure, in relation to Size.

The evidence of that relation, though in great measure disguised by the secondary effects of internal ventilation and cambial activity in all the higher vegetation of the land, appears with cumulative reiteration in the primary structure, as described in detail in the preceding chapters. Behind it all stands the principle of similarity, affecting organisms that are essentially accumulators, and show the result of this in their steadily increasing primary dimensions. The most obvious sign of it is seen in the obconical form of the primary axis, with its progressive complexity of structure. But like results may be expected also in the petiole and in the root, when the structure of smaller examples is compared with that seen in those of larger size. Thus the vascular plant affords three separate tests of the effect of Size upon internal primary structure. If the principle of similarity has actually been effective in determining structure as the size increases, cognate results should appear in them all : as in fact they do.

The relation of Size to Structure is closely connected with the proportion of the surfaces of transit to the bulk contained by them : and so it touches the whole foundation of the physiology of nutrition and of transfer of material. It finds its most ready illustration in the comparative study of the primary conducting tracts, which show increasing elaboration of form as the size advances. These are in fact plastic in relation to size, and illustrate in various ways how the proportion of surface to bulk may be thereby maintained. The result is not, however, a positive increase upon the original proportion. At best the advantage gained is only a partial set off against the contingent loss consequent upon increasing size. In definite examples it may be estimated as amounting to about one half of the actual loss of proportion of surface to bulk. Such changes of form have been illustrated at length in Chapters II to X, for the leading types of primitive vascular plants. The results may now be drawn together into a comprehensive statement, which gains in effect by the extent and essential uniformity of the facts upon which it is based.

I. THE PRIMARY CONDUCTING TRACTS

In the simplest Pteridophytes generally, and more particularly in their sporelings, the conducting tract consists of a solid strand of tracheids surrounded by tissue of the nature of phloem, and delimited from the surrounding tissue by a layer of cells more or less clearly defined as endodermis. The comparisons of the simpler with the more complex types have here been chiefly based upon the primary xylem, since the surface by which the dead tracheids face the living cells that surround the wood is a clearly defined surface of transit, as well marked in many fossils as it is in living plants. Measurement of the stele itself need not be taken into account at the moment, for it raises more complicated questions than does the limiting surface of the dead tracheids.[1]

The woody column is in the first instance minute : its mean diameter may be measured in tenths or hundredths of a millimeter.[2] It is from such minute beginnings that the comparison starts. In sporelings the column is purely tracheidal, with irregularly circular outline as seen in transverse section : and most of the tracheids though not necessarily all are in contact with living cells. In primitive plants, and particularly in early fossils, as the individual develops upwards, the woody tract expands simply by increase in number of the tracheids, thus forming an enlarged solid core of roughly cylindrical form : this attained large size in some types of *Lepidodendron*, and in *Thamnopteris*. But so simple a structure is exceptional, and no large

---

[1] The term ' surface ' is here understood to be based upon a rough measure of the pitted walls of the tracheids as a whole : but the area of the pit-membranes themselves, so often enlarged where they face upon living cells, constitute the actual surface specially involved in transit. The more accurate estimates of the future will have to take this into account.

[2] In Wardlaw's smallest section of *Psilotum* (Fig. 3, i) it is less than 0·02 mm. in a young plant of *Tmesipteris* (Holloway, *Trans. N.Z. Inst.* vol. 1, p. 32, Fig. 84), it is 0·08 mm. in a sporeling of *Anemia* (*Ferns*, vol. ii, Fig. 443, ii) it is about 0·06 mm. in *Rhynia*, presumably in an adult state, it is 0·156 (Kidston and Lang, No. I, Pl. VII. Fig. 43).

plants possessing purely tracheidal wood are known living to-day. It has been shown in the preceding chapters, for plants now living and in many fossils, how the proportion of surface-exposure of the dead tracheidal tissue to the living cells has tended to be maintained, as against the contingent loss of proportion of surface to bulk that would necessarily follow as the size increases, if a purely tracheidal tract were simply enlarged as such. The methods by which this is effected vary in detail : but they may be summarised under the following heads :

(A) By *Medullation*, forming a central pith.

(B) By *Sculpturing* of the outer surface of the woody tract, which may take various forms, such as that of deep fluting.

(C) By complete *Disintegration* of the xylic mass, as it appears in transverse section.

(D) By general *Vitalisation*, living cells being scattered throughout the xylic mass.

In practice these various methods are not found to be sharply distinct from one another : moreover they are often combined so that the xylic tract may approach in divers ways to that ideal state where each tracheid forms contact with one or more living cells. This is the condition prevalent in modern types of wood : but it was not the condition usual in Palaeozoic time. In tracing the steps which have led to it we shall be following an evolutionary history of high physiological moment. Each of the methods may first be examined comparatively, and the part considered which it takes in upholding the proportion of surface to bulk of the tracheal tissue as the xylic tract increases.

(A) MEDULLATION

The conversion of centrally-lying tracheids of an enlarging tracheidal core into thin-walled parenchyma, thus forming pith, is a fact which may be followed comparatively in many distinct evolutionary lines : but it is best seen in certain fossils. It is not restricted to axes : the xylem of roots may also be medullated. This fact suggests that the change is not dependent upon the insertion of appendages. In relatively primitive plants it probably owed its origin to a change of destination of certain procambial cells from the tracheid-nature, as seen in the solid protostele, to that of parenchyma. The process may be wholly intra-stelar, and comparison shows it to have been polyphyletic. Its origin is suggested by the structure seen in some of the larger protosteles, such as the fossil Lycopods and Osmundaceæ, which appear to have followed a parallel course structurally. A distinction arises first between the outer and inner primary wood : the former is more directly continuous with the leaf-traces, and so it will act functionally as conducting wood : this is the region which is retained after medullation. The inner wood, not being so directly related to the leaf-traces (if present), tends to become a place of water-storage. It would be immaterial for that function whether the tissue-elements are thick or thin walled, and replacement of tracheids by parenchyma would be economical. Whether or not this be the true physiological explanation, it accords with the structural facts as seen in large protosteles. In particular the state described as ' mixed pith,' where storage-tracheids and parenchyma are intermixed, provides strong evidence of its truth, and leads up to the solenoxylic state frequent in primitive Ferns and Lycopods.

The relation of such medullation to size is neither exact nor obligatory in early fossils at large. It may, however, be shown in favourable examples that a relation does exist, by comparison of sections of stems of the same species : as in *Lepidodendron Wunschianum* (see Table, p. 50). Here medullation appears only in steles of relatively large size. On the other hand, a progressive relation of pith-formation to size is illustrated in the ontogeny of many plants now living : for instance in the sporelings of Ferns (*Loxsoma.*

Gleichenia pectinata. Thompson, *Trans. R. S. Edin.* vol. lii, p. 715. *Pteris incisa,* Bower, *Studies* vii, *Ann. of Bot.* xxxii, p. 28), and *Selaginella spinosa* (Bower, *Ann. of Bot.* vol. xxv, Pl. XLVII).

In most modern vascular plants medullation appears so early in the ontogeny, and has gone so far, that the vestiges of the story are disguised or lost, and the relation of medullation to size is not evident. But certain experiments by Flaskämper on Leguminous roots bear on the point (*Flora,* 1910, p. 205). The thick primary root of the Broad Bean is normally medullated. He found that by removing the cotyledons after the first days of germination, and thus starving the roots, the pith disappeared from the contracted stele with its greatly diminished number of tracheæ: but as the plumular leaves became functional and nutrition was restored, the normally medullated structure reappeared in the distal region. These experiments showed that, even in the individual, a size-relation exists dependent on nutrition. It is desirable that they should be repeated, with a view to establishing that relation in detail, and in varied examples.

The general conclusion which follows from this brief comparative study of medullation in early and in later vascular plants is that progressive steps are illustrated ontogenetically, and also stratigraphically, though the demonstration of this is not always decisive : that they are due to conversion of a central region of the wood into parenchymatous pith : that the change accompanies large size of the xylic tract, though with no exact numerical relation : and that the pith may originate within the barrier of an uninterrupted endodermis. As regards the effect of medullation upon the surface-area of dead wood facing upon living cells, a mixed pith and finally a solenoxylic state will certainly tend to maintain the balance of tracheidal surface to bulk in an enlarging stele. But so long as the xylic ring is complete the physiological effect would not be so great as when medullation is combined with other changes, and particularly with the disintegration of the ring of wood. By this the outer and inner living regions would be brought into relation, so as to constitute a connected system. This highly derivative structure is the prevalent state in modern types, and particularly in the Seed-Plants.

(B) SCULPTURING

The simplest way of increasing the primary wood of an enlarging plant or race of plants would be by magnifying the primitive strand without any change of form or structure. Early fossils adopted this simple plan : we see it in the cylindrical stele of *Lepidodendron*, and of certain primitive Ferns. But in accordance with the principle of similarity this would bring with it the disability of a fall in the proportion of surface of the dead tracheidal tissue to its bulk : thus there would be a constantly diminishing relation of it as a whole to the living tissue that surrounds it. It need then be no matter for surprise that plants such as the simpler Lepidodendroids, the Botryopterideæ, and such large Fern-types as *Thamnopteris* have all died out, while no large plant is known to exist to-day in which this ineffective structure persists.

A remedy is found in sculpturing of the outer surface of the woody tract. Any elaboration of form from the simple cylinder will tend to level up the loss of proportion of surface to bulk contingent on increasing size. This gives a special interest to the study of the modifications of form of the woody column. The actual form which the column takes is determined in the procambial region, by the destination of cells or tracts of cells as tracheids or as parenchyma respectively. The appearance when mature may suggest intrusion of parenchyma into the woody column, but the detail of development does not support such an explanation.

The forms assumed by the xylic tract are various : for instance in *Lycopodium* it may appear as a complex sponge (Chap. III) : in the simpler species of *Selaginella* as a flattened ribbon (Chap. IV) : but the most characteristic form is that of the fluted column which gives in transverse section a stellate outline. The number of rays of the star and the depth of the involutions between them may vary : but a general relation has been established between those variations and the size of the whole tract : the larger the size the deeper the involutions, and the more numerous the rays (Figs. 4, 6, 21, 55). These elaborations of form appear in parts of divers category, and in plants of no near affinity one to another. Hence they may be held as homoplastic, and the stellate appearance in transverse section is no safe index of affinity. They appear to be adaptations tending to secure a certain physiological result. In any case their effect is to enhance the surface-exposure of the enlarged woody tract beyond what it would have been if the form had been cylindrical. Though the outline of the stele as defined by the endodermis often remains cylindrical, it not infrequently follows the sculpturing of the xylic tract, particularly where the stele is large (Figs. 9, 59-61).

(C) DISINTEGRATION

The xylem may often appear in transverse section as a single continuous tract, even when sculptured : this is so in primitive forms ; it is so in some Lycopods, and often in *Psilotum* and *Tmesipteris* : also in certain primitive Ferns. It may, on the other hand—and particularly in more recent forms—show a greater or less degree of disintegration, so that a number of distinct masses of xylem appear in the transverse section : these may, however, fuse above or below the surface of section, as in *Lycopodium*, forming a xylem sponge. The phloem and endodermis may or may not follow suit : if they do the state is described as polystelic—or better, *meristelic,* for each tract is a part of the original stele, and is constructed more or less like it. This is the state presented by most modern Leptosporangiate Ferns, and in some of the large Selaginellas ; while it probably applies also to the primary conducting tracts of the Medulloseæ. There is reason to believe that this meristelic state has been attained along polyphyletic lines. In the Pteridophytes it is seen to arise in the ontogeny in relation to increasing size, and it may be regarded as a further adaptive elaboration of the conducting tracts where secondary cambial growth is absent. It is certainly the fact that the greater isolation of the xylic-masses gives an increased surface-exposure. Where the phloem and endodermis follow suit the result is a direct relation of the cortex to the centrally-lying parenchyma, with enhanced ventilation by continuous intercellular spaces as a consequence. Many facts and measurements relating to meristelic disintegration will be found in Chapters III and VIII which relate respectively to *Selaginella,* and to the Leptosporangiate Ferns.

(D) VITALISATION

By ' Vitalisation ' of the wood is meant the intimate contact of dead tracheids with living cells. In its highest perfection the whole xylic tract is thoroughly permeated by a living system, so that in transverse section the living and dead constituents appear in approximately equal proportions. The difference between this state, which is characteristic of modern wood, and the purely tracheidal tracts of many primitive types and particularly of many extinct fossils, has never been sufficiently insisted upon. Attention was drawn to it by Williams in its relation to the Size Factor.[1] A full state of vitalisation has usually been attained by gradual steps, and in various ways in the

---

[1] *Proc. R. S. Edin.* vol. xlv, 1925, p. 286. He noted that in Ferns purely tracheidal wood is only to be found in the adult in certain fossils, and in some primitive living types, such as *Osmunda.*

course of evolution of the primary stele : such steps may frequently be reflected in the ontogeny. Medullation, sculpturing, and disintegration are all related closely to it, and contribute to the final result. It may be regarded as the sum of them all. It appears to have been a necessary condition for the enlargement of the individual stele to the highest dimensions : for instance, the huge primary stele of *Sutcliffia* is thoroughly permeated by parenchyma, while it is significant that the extreme dilation of the stele seen in the larger Palms is accompanied by its thorough permeation by living tissue (see Chapter IX). On the other hand, vitalisation is present in high degree in secondary tissues.

This classification of the methods of structural advance in the conducting tract is arbitrary, and the distinctions between them are not clearly defined. In actual practice they are seen to overlap, and to co-operate in producing the complex state seen where the Size is great. The point which they have in common is that they all tend to maintain the collective surface of presentation of tracheids to living cells : so that as the conducting tract increases there shall be a structural set-off against the contingent loss of proportion of surface to bulk. Attempts to measure the effect of structural changes actually observed, in leading to this end, were made by Wardlaw in his analysis of sections taken serially from the same shoots respectively of *Psilotum*, of *Tmesipteris*, and of certain species of *Lycopodium* (Chapters II, III). The result of these may be stated in general terms. On passing in such plants as these from the small and simple xylem-tract below to the larger and disintegrated wood above, the fall in ratio of surface to bulk is markedly less that it would have been if the approximately cylindrical form had been maintained. In point of fact it appears that about 50 per cent. of the contingent loss of proportion is saved. *It may thus be concluded that, assuming the maintenance of a high ratio of surface to bulk to be of functional importance, there is an advantage in the increasing complication of form as against any mere magnification of the original image : but the structural changes do not wholly suffice to preserve the original ratio of surface to bulk.*

Such estimates are necessarily rough, and it is desirable that they should be extended. They are put forward provisionally, till more refined methods shall give more exact results, not only for primary but also for secondary conducting tissues.

II. ENDODERMIS

The Endodermis was noted in the Introductory Chapter as the second of the three important limiting surfaces present in the construction of vascular plants. It shuts off the primary conducting tracts from the surrounding tissues, and in the first instance follows their outlines as a continuous investment : but its relation to the surface of the xylic tract is not constant. Its structure is such as to give it protoplasmic control over the transit of soluble materials while the close fitting of its cells together makes it an impervious gas-barrier. The tissues within and without frequently bear evidence by their contents of the effectiveness of its power of control (Fig. 62).

The form of the primary stele being habitually conical, its bulk increases upwards as the cube, while the surface of the enclosing endodermis will increase only as the square of the linear dimensions. Consequently, so far as endodermal control is of importance, a similar question will arise for the endodermis as for the limiting surface of the tracheal tract. It might then be anticipated that where the contour of the woody column is elaborated in relation to increasing size, that of the endodermis would follow its outlines. It frequently does so : but not always in detail. Prominent instances of non-conformity of the endodermal outline to that of the xylem are seen in roots, where not-withstanding the deep fluting or segregation of the latter the endodermis habitually preserves a smooth cylindrical outline. The same holds for the fluted steles of the Psilo-taceæ, and for the various stelar developments in *Lyco-podium*. Frequently, however, the endodermis follows the sculpturing and even the disintegration of the xylem, forming with the phloem a complete investment of each

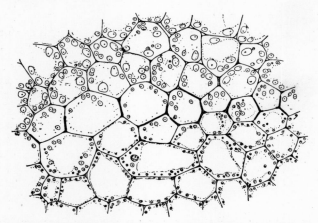

FIG. 62.—*Helminthostachys zeylanica* : part of a transverse section of a root. The endodermis, recognised by the characteristic structure of the radial walls, marks a boundary between the cortex with large starch grains (here above), and the conjunctive parenchyma with small starch grains (here below). Drawn by Dr. J. McL. Thompson. (× 44.)

xylic tract. In the Leptosporangiate Ferns this is habitu-ally seen, whether in axis or in petiole (Figs. 41, 43, 45) : also in those species of *Selaginella* in which the stele is disintegrated (Fig. 9).

There are, however, further facts relating to the endo-dermis which appear to be clearly dependent upon rela-tively large size. It has been shown that where roots are large the cylindrical form of the stele may be departed from, giving a corrugated outline in transverse section : as in *Philodendron Adansoni* (Fig. 59). In large Palm-roots a similar corrugation of the surface appears, which increases with size till it leads to disruption of the endodermis at the points of deepest involution. This was seen to lead in the extreme case of *Verschaffeltia* where the stele is 25 mm. in diameter, to a high state of disintegration (Fig. 61). A parallel to this appears in the large stems of *Osmundites skidegatensis* and *O. Carnieri*, with steles respectively 25 mm. and 35 mm. in diameter (Fig. 30). These stems are in fact of approximately the same dimensions as the roots of *Verschaffeltia*. In both the endodermal barrier is interrupted, and a free relation of the cortex to the interior of the stele is established. A normal endodermis is by its structure a gas-barrier, and as such it would intervene between the ventilating system of the cortex and that within the stele. This condition may be tolerable where the size is small ; but it would become increasingly difficult as the size increases and the proportion of surface to bulk diminishes. The interruptions of the barrier may be held as concessions to increasing size in all of the plants here quoted. A common ventilating system of the part would thus be established in place of two partial systems.

III. PLASTICITY OF STELAR TRACTS IN STEM AND LEAF

The plasticity of the primary stele finds its climax in the Leptosporangiate Ferns (Chapter VIII). In them the continuity of the endodermal sheath shows that the complete enclosure of their conducting tracts is a matter of physiological importance, and the problem will be to secure elaboration of the stele without any break of that continuity. The danger-points of leakage would be at the departure of each leaf-trace from the primary stele, and at the point of transition from solenoxyly to full solenostely : more particularly the latter. In the sporeling, after a period of development with increasing pith there follows the advent of internal phloem, a state which is permanently retained in the type of stele seen in *Lindsaya*. But with further increase in size, solenostely follows, as in *Odontosoria* (Fig. 35). First a series of successively deeper axillary pockets are formed by involution of the endodermis : then a sudden structural change takes place, the endodermis being continued across the whole width of the pith, cutting off the intra-stelar region that lies below it from that which is above : the latter is now continuous with the cortex (Fig. 63). From this point onwards the central tract of the pith becomes physiologically extra-stelar, though in the ontogeny the part below the barrier was intra-stelar. The sudden structural change is opportunist in character rather than conformable to morphological rule.

The change may be held as justified by the functional advantages that follow from it. In the first place, the complete solenostely thus established allows of a common ventilation-system extending from the cortex through the foliar gaps to the central column, which is geographically intra-stelar, but now physiologically extra-stelar. Secondly it doubles the surface-presentment of the stelar tract to the ventilated parenchyma, so important as size increases : for the solenostele has endodermis on both sides. Moreover, by enlarge-ment of the stelar ring, which is a marked feature as a rule so soon as the solenostele is established, the xylic

FIG. 63.—Plan of the stelar construction of a young plant of *Gleichenia pectinata*, after Dr. J. McL. Thompson. It shows in median section the way in which the stele enlarges conic-ally upwards, and widens into a solenostele with leaf-gaps.

ring can be thinned out, sometimes to a single row of tracheids, so as to give high surface-presentment of the dead tracheids to living cells. These considerations suggest that in that puzzling structure, the solenostele, we see a biological adjustment, which makes large size functionally easy for a conducting tract completely enclosed by endodermis. A like argument, *mutatis mutandis*, will apply to the solenostely of *Selaginella*, and temporarily as a passing stage in the leafless tubers of *Nephrolepis*. These examples show that it may occur in microphyllous, or even in leafless shoots, and thus *that solenostely is essentially a phenomenon of purely stelar adjustment*.

Once solenostely is established in the stem, all further sculpturing connoted by dictyostely, polycycly, and perforation simply elaborates the scheme thus initiated. Wonderful as the final results in Ferns may be, in showing to what lengths the plasticity of the conducting tracts of the axis may attain as the size enlarges, they present no further features that are essentially new.

The elaboration of the petiolar meristele as size increases has followed lines of its own. It appears in its most distinctive form in the Ferns. Here, excepting in certain extinct fossils, the leaf is a definitely dorsiventral organ, and this symmetry is deeply impressed upon its meristele. The Osmundaceæ, whether living or fossil, demonstrate in their ontogeny how the meristele, originally oval in section, is flattened out into a broad, continuous, strongly channelled or gutter-shaped strap. In many smaller-leaved types its form is flat : but commonly it is gutter-shaped, the concavity being adaxial. The meristele thus channelled forms the starting point for further elaborations according to size. The most marked is its lateral involution along lines opposite to the linear pneumathodes, the effect of which is to extend the ventilated cortex deeply towards the centre of the leaf-stalk : the depth of the involution is often in proportion to size (Fig. 45). Another feature is the approach of the inwardly-hooked margins closely to one another : occasionally in large petioles these actually join, forming a complete ring, like a solenostele, though this has originated along quite distinct lines from that of the stem : a complete ring may be seen in large leaves of *Pteris podophylla* where the meristele reaches 20 mm. in diameter (see *Studies*, vii, Text, Fig. 28, *Ann. of Bot.* xxxii, p. 40). The effect will then be to sever the internal parenchyma from the cortex, offering a complete gas-barrier, but open at its ends. On the other hand, such barriers are commonly partial only, and when large they are liable to be interrupted by perforations which allow of ready communication, as in the leaves of the larger Tree Ferns (Fig. 45, 6).

A further consequence of the gutter-like curvature of the meristele is its effect upon the insertion of the pinna-traces. In small-leaved types with a flat meristele, these spring naturally from the margins to supply the lateral rows of pinnae. But where the curvature is strong, as it is in larger leaves, the pinna-traces slip as it were, from the margins to the outer convex surface becoming, as it is described, extra-marginal. That this is merely a plastic concession to the curvature of the meristele, consequent on greater size, is shown by the fact that in the individual leaf their insertion may be extra-marginal in the large rachis where the meristele is strongly curved ; but distally, where being small it flattens out, the insertion becomes marginal, as is seen in *Gymnogramme* (*Trismeria*) *trifoliata* (J. McL. Thompson, *Trans. R. S. Edin.* lii, pp. 381-384). Thus perforation of the meristele, and superficial insertion of the pinna-traces upon it, may both be held as secondary consequences of the extreme widening out and curvature of the petiolar meristele.

But it may be asked, why should the gutter-like form be assumed at all ? Probably there may not have been only one determining cause, but one potent factor appears to have been the maintenance of a due proportion of surface to bulk of the tracheidal tissue, and this is secured by widening of the enlarging meristele which has to be adjusted within a firm resistant rind.

A good example is presented by the meristeles of successive leaves of *Thamnopteris*, the bases of which are cut through in the well-known section photographed (× 2) by K. and G. V. (*Fossil Osmundaceæ*, iii, Pl. I, *Trans. R. S. Edin.* vol. xlvi). Traces of these meristeles are shown in their natural size in Fig. 64. The width of the xylem in

FIG. 64. — Meristeles of *Thamnopteris* traced from the type specimen, and reduced to natural size, showing the actual dimensions as the trace passes outwards into the leaf-base.

the largest (6) of these, when flattened into a plane, is about 18 times the width of the smallest (1) and, as the photographs on their Plates IV and V show in detail, the mass of purely tracheidal wood becomes gradually thinner as the width increases, till it finally consists of no more than 2 to 4 layers of tracheids. This wide but attenuated band has to be accommodated within a sclerotic sheath that measures in its inner diameter little more than one half the width of the meristele, and becoming channelled it can fit itself into that limited space. Such structure finds its parallel in the stems of *Selaginella*, where also there is a widening ribbon within a firm rind (Chapter III). In *S. Willdenovii* it has been seen that the widening stele becomes convoluted within its resistant barrier : so in the meristele of Ferns the gutter-shaped curve adjusts the widening strap to the restricted space available within the rind. But if this were the reason for the channelled form, would it not be possible that the concavity might be either adaxial or abaxial ? The former appears constant for living Ferns, but early fossils, grouped as the ' Inversicatenales,' illustrate the latter. In *Anachoropteris* not only is the curvature reversed, being abaxial ; but also the insertion of the pinna-traces has slipped from the margin and appears superficial :

their place is now, however, on the adaxial face of the meristele, not as in Leptosporangiate Ferns on its abaxial face (Fig. 65, 3). All this is readily intelligible on the theory of the widening strap, whereby a due proportion of surface exposure of the tracheidal tissue is maintained : though it is forced into curvature, either adaxial or abaxial, by the barrier of the resistant rind.

But this does not exhaust the instances of the plasticity of the petiolar meristele : there remain the meristeles of the Zygopterideæ. These have been referred in origin to a ' Clepsydroid ' type, where the meristele is a simple strap, oval in section (Chapter VI). Here it will suffice to quote for comparison the extreme case of *Ankyropteris West-phaliensis* (Fig. 24), and to recall the four ' antennae,' two adaxial and two abaxial ; these curve so as to complete a peripheral ring with the exception of narrow gaps running along the two faces. The effect of the whole is again the maintenance of a high proportion of surface to bulk of the tracheidal mass, while it is tucked compactly within the resistant rind. The biological conditions are like those in the Leptosporangiate Ferns, but the result is worked out with independent detail along a distinct phyletic line.

In the plastic moulding of the primary vascular tracts of the Pteridophyta, as large size is attained, an approach has been made along four quite distinct lines of evolution towards a hollow cylinder. This is far removed from the centre of the part, which was the position occupied by the protostele of the small stem, or by the central meristele of the small petiole. All the structural changes seen accompany increase in size, and the facts indicate that the consequent *decentralisation, whether of axis or leaf, is related to Size* (Fig. 65). The result may be traced along four distinct lines, with convergent consequences : viz. (i) the soleno-stelic stem, as seen in Ferns, and in certain Selaginellas : (ii) the adaxially curved meristele in the petiole of large

Leptosporangiate Ferns, the ring being sometimes completed : (iii) the abaxially curved meristele of the ' Inversicatenales,' as seen in *Anachoropteris* : (iv) the Zygopterid petiolar meristele with ' antennae,' as in *A. Westphaliensis*. The fact is that the hollow cylinder, provided it be thin, is one of those forms which present a very large surface-exposure. It cannot be by accident that such parallels

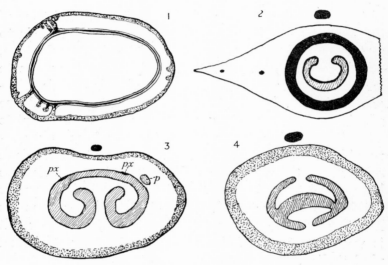

FIG. 65.—Diagrammatic drawings showing various types of decentralisation of the vascular tracts. They are not drawn exactly to the same scale. 1, Rhizome of *Cibotium Barometz*, showing a large and attenuated solenostele. 2, Leaf-base of *Osmundites Kolbei* after Gwynne-Vaughan (*Foss. Osm.* IV, p. 460), showing adaxially curved meristele within a sclerotic ring. 3, Transverse section of petiole of *Anachoropteris rotundata*, from Scott, *Studies*, Fig. 158, showing abaxially curved meristele : the width of the stelar ribbon is to the diameter of the petiole as 12 to 8. *px*=protoxylem : *p*=pinna-trace. 4, Transverse section of petiole of *Ankyropteris Westphaliensis* from Scott, *Studies*, Fig. 135. The total width of the meristele, including the ' middle-band ' is to the diameter of the petiole as 3 to 2. The black dot in 2, 3, 4 indicates the direction of the axis.

arise in large organisms so distinct from one another as those cited. A common causality will probably underlie them : and among the circumstances that have been effective may be reckoned the need for maintenance of a due surface-exposure of the enlarging tracheidal tracts, while the existence of a firm rind controls the form which the enlarging tract shall take.

It is possible thus to see biological significance even in the most elaborate of those forms which the primary conducting tracts assume in the absence of cambial increase. We may recognise that increasing Size will have been at least one determining factor in producing such high plasticity as they exhibit. At the same time the fact that the examples appear in petioles as well as in axes, and often with the minimum of relation to the insertion of appendages, will indicate that the conducting tracts are subject to formative influences that act independently of the relation of parts.

IV. CAMBIAL THICKENING

It will have been obvious from the structural shifts to which the more primitive vascular plants have resorted so as to accommodate a primary conducting tract to increasing Size, that this would ultimately become an unworkable proposition : in point of fact none of them have attained the largest size while dependent upon primary tissues only. If full advantage is to be taken of the continued apical growth which they all possess, with its geometrical ratio of increase of accessory shoots and leaves, some provision must be made for automatic increase of the conducting tracts. The apical cone itself cannot be depended upon to provide it directly, though gallant efforts to this end have been made by the largest Tree Ferns, and by the Palms (Chapter IX). This is the office of a secondary meristem— the Cambium. The common incidence of the demand has produced a wide response. No class of Vascular Plants is entirely without secondary thickening : there is reason to believe that it has been polyphyletic in its origin, and once established it can be continued indefinitely. The giant trunks of the Gymnosperms and Dicotyledons are a sufficient witness to its effectiveness, up to the limit of mechanical stability.

A feature present in secondary vascular tissues, which has probably contributed in high degree to their functional success, is the presence of rays of living parenchyma. The woody tissues that they traverse may be purely tracheidal, as they are generally in Palaeozoic fossils with cambial growth : but even here the number and distribution of the rays brings the result that the secondary wood is efficiently vitalised, even in very ancient types. As time went on the living system permeating the secondary wood was further perfected by the transverse division of certain cambium-cells of tracheidal form, and their retention of vitality as wood-parenchyma. As the cambial thickening proceeds the endodermis surrounding the original conducting tract is obliterated and ventilation, no longer impeded by its presence, leads deep into the woody column by means of intercellular spaces traversing the medullary rays. The progress towards this physiologically effective condition may be worked out in varying detail in Gymnosperms and Dicotyledons : but the net result is the same for all. The indefinitely enlarging plant is thus supplied with a conducting column constructed on a plan that is capable of unlimited expansion. It meets the three leading requirements automatically, as their demands themselves increase : viz. for adequate mechanical strength, conduction, and ventilated storage-space.

This is not the place to discuss at length the physiological functions of the parenchymatous system that permeates the conducting tracts, and particularly the secondary wood. The importance of its presence has been fully recognised by physiologists. It was the foundation of the views of Godlewski (*Pringsh-Jahrb*, 1884, Bd. XV, p. 569). Haberlandt after describing its anatomical relation to the vascular tissue sums up thus : ' The anatomical data certainly point to one of two conclusions : either the xylem-parenchyma and the medullary rays assist in the conduction of water, or else the vessels and tracheids take part in the translocation of carbohydrates. The two views are not mutually incompatible, and it is quite possible that they are both correct ' (*Physiol. Plant Anatomy*, Engl. Edn. p. 673). More recently H. H. Dixon writes as follows : ' We thus come to regard the wood as a specialised reservoir of liquid food-stuffs within the plant. . . . Maintenance of the large and diffuse living body of the plant requires a large surface of interchange between the living body and this reservoir. This large surface is provided (1) by bast, (2) the tongue-like medullary rays penetrating into the wood, and (3) their extensions, the wood-parenchyma, intermingled with the tracheids and surrounding vessels. These tissues are not only charged with the functions of introducing substances into this reservoir and of abstracting materials from the currents which pass in it, but also are most probably responsible for the duty of keeping the tracheæ viable by removing precipitates and coagulations and by preventing the formation of gels.' These references will suffice to show the high importance now attached by physiologists to the vitalisation of the secondary wood by its continuous system of parenchyma. From the facts embodied in this book we see that the highly vitalised state of the wood present in modern trees was not inherent in early vascular plants. Their ' first intention ' was physiologically impracticable, except on a small scale : for it consisted in simple enlargement of the primary tracheidal tract. Its necessary vitalisation was gradually achieved in relation to increasing size, and the palæontological evidence shows that the method of trial and error played its part in the process. Coincidently or alternatively cambial thickening arose, first with simple vitalisation by medullary rays,[1] but later with that more complete linking

---

[1] Secondary production of wood without medullary rays is possible, but it appears in any case to have been rare. The ' outer ' wood of *Schizopodium*, and possibly the nodal wood of *Equisetum* may be quoted as intermediate conditions, where medullary rays are of rudimentary type or absent (Harris, *Schizopodium Davidi*, *Phil. Trans.* vol. ccxvii, 1929, p. 395).

up of a living system that is seen in modern trees. It is this result, combined with continued apical development and cambial growth, that has made the largest dendroid structure possible. The evolutionary progression was probably polyphyletic : vestiges still remain to show that it was so.[1]

V. EXTERNAL SURFACE AND VENTILATION

The external surface of the plant-body is the third of those important limiting tissue-surfaces, mentioned in the introductory chapter, as suitable subjects for observation from the point of view of the proportion of surface to bulk as the size increases. All physiological commerce with the outer world passes through it : accordingly, so far as the transit through it is proportional to the surface, the maintenance of the collective area exposed will be a matter of moment in any enlarging plant. This is not the place for any detailed discussion of the degree of its permeability as affected by the structure of the surface-walls. It must suffice to contrast the soft absorptive surface of a root-hair, of a submerged Alga, or of a fungal hypha with the cuticularised surface of an exposed sub-aerial shoot. We thus realise the broad differences of character which such walls possess : and we may correlate these on the one hand with the medium to which each is exposed, and on the other with the demands which would naturally follow upon the form assumed. It will be necessary to bear in mind that in each individual case a due proportion of receptive surface to bulk must be maintained. Such an outlook as this is essential to a rational understanding of external Morphology. Thus Form may be related to the most inevitable of those factors which have influenced its development, viz. Size. In applying this view it will be well for the moment to discard entirely those more advanced sub-aerial

[1] Scott, ' The Old Wood and the New,' *New Phyt.* vol. i.

plants in which internal ventilation is highly developed, and to examine first those more primitive types which have a less differentiated structure, and a generally receptive external surface.

Gametophytes generally will fall under this heading, as well as the more primitive sporophytes. The linear filament is the fundamental structure. Wherever it is retained in Algae or Fungi it secures these plants against any pressing problems of proportion of surface to bulk. Even where elaborations of form and structure lead to a massive thallus the Algae commonly maintain a relatively large proportion of exposed surface by means of their flattened form, and particularly by distal hairs, or by tufts of hairs. Much may be learned by study of the Thallophytes from this aspect. But it is in the Bryophytes that the maintenance of a due proportion of surface to bulk finds illustrations which may be held as specially illuminating in relation to leafy land-plants at large. All sub-aerial plants develop under conflicting factors that primarily affect their form. It is a legitimate scientific method to concentrate attention upon a single factor, and from that aspect to see how far the natural requirements have been actually met, in the development of representative examples. More particularly is this permissible where the factor in question is immanent and unavoidable, as is that of Size.

The formation of a Moss-bud upon any protonemal filament may serve as a simple illustration. The first product of germination is the photosynthetic filament. As Von Goebel has shown, when grown in feeble light protonema may develop as such indefinitely : this may be held as a starved state. But under normal conditions of nourishment it sooner or later forms pear-shaped buds, more massive than the filament, and with more complex segmentation. Each segment may grow out into a flattened leaf, and a leafy Moss-bud is the result. The leaf-formation follows on increase in bulk, and the complex leafy form gives enhanced surface-exposure, which may be held as a set-off against the contingent loss of proportion of surface to bulk as the massive bud is developed. It is possible to extend this view to leaves at large, and to see in foliar development generally a similar reaction of Form to the requirements of increasing Size. Such reaction may be presented by any enlarging type of organism. From this point of view leaves may then be held as homoplastic responses to the demands of increasing Size. Until their origin by common descent in any specific cases compared shall have been proved, a polyphyletic view of the origin of leaves would thus appear to be a tenable proposition.

A formation of simple leaves, for the most part a single cell-layer in thickness, suffices for small Mosses. But in large types such as *Polytrichum*, where the structure is more massive, the blade bears on its upper surface longitudinal plates of chlorophyll-parenchyma. These may, it is true, be effective in collecting and retaining water during rain, but it is indisputable that they also give increased surface-exposure, with enhanced opportunity for external ventilation under control. Moreover the feature is characteristic of large Mosses, in which internal ventilation does not exist. A parallel effect, though not alike in detailed structure, is seen in the more massive thalloid Liverworts, such as the Marchantiaceæ. Here again the appearance is as of a folding of the outer surface, though it has been found that splitting of anticlinal walls may also take its share (*Reinhard Orth. Flora*, Bd. 124, p. 152). Into the air-chambers thus formed green assimilating cells project, and divide : thus greatly elaborating the exposed surface of the cavity. Such methods of increasing surface-exposure in relatively massive tissues of the gametophyte that are otherwise unventilated, have their obvious use. But they are sporadic, and in point of efficiency stand far behind that regular internal ventilation which is characteristic of most sub-aerial sporophytes. They may be held as tentative concessions to the need for a due proportion of surface to bulk in a massive photosynthetic plant exposed to the air.

The introduction of internal ventilation of the tissues of the sporophyte, with openings to the atmosphere through stomata and lenticels, made possible that degree of exposure of photosynthetic cells to gaseous interchange upon which all the more advanced land-vegetation is based. Its great advantage lies in the fact that not only is the exposure subject to stomatal control, but also that this is secured in parts that are themselves relatively massive, and so are protected from undue evaporation, and are relatively resistant to mechanical risks. There is no need to consider this in detail here as regards the mesophyll, for the point has been fully discussed by Haberlandt as illustrating the Principle of Maximum Exposure (*Phys. Plant Anatomy*, Engl. Edn. p. 276, etc.).

The converse state as presented by submerged leaves raises the question of the effect of this habit upon form and surface-exposure. What would be its morphological effect upon plants belonging to families typically sub-aerial? Since stomata are absent from submerged parts, the gaseous interchange can now be conducted only through the outer surface, and the internal ventilation-system is thus sealed up. An increase in proportion of surface to bulk of the tissues enclosed by it would be advantageous, and some further elaboration of form would be a means ready to hand for securing it. As a matter of fact this is illustrated by the submerged leaves of isolated genera belonging to many distinct families. A high degree of dissection of the blade is the feature seen in the submerged leaves of *Hottonia* among the Primulaceæ, of the Batrachian Ranunculi, and of *Ceratophyllum* : while simple terete or narrowly flattened blades appear in *Potamogeton pectinatus*, and other submerged Naiads. In *Aponogeton fenestralis*, a denizen of still waters, the broad blade is perforated, which gives practically a like result. Provided the thickness of these leaves is not increased, the elaboration of form will necessarily have the effect of raising the proportion of surface to the bulk of the tissue within. That the form is correlated with the medium is shown by *Cabomba* and *Ranunculus heterophyllus*, in which the submerged leaves are finely cut, while those that are subaerial have a more coherent blade. In all of these the increased proportion of surface-exposure which follows from the modification of form is a feature that cannot be neglected, and should not be minimised. Any objection to this as an adaptive change, which may be based upon the co-existence of submerged plants having broad leaves with those that have highly dissected leaves, is irrelevant. The co-existence of broad submerged leaves with those that are dissected is no more valid argument against the latter form being adaptive, than is the co-existence of standard trees and climbers in a forest a valid argument against the adaptive adjustment of the latter to a climbing habit. Such differences of form, while subject to the same conditions, indicate divergence of adaptability, not the absence of adaptation in any one of them.

A point of morphological interest presented by such data in the present discussion lies in the fact that dissection or fenestration of submerged leaves offers a formal parallel with the meristely and perforation of the primary conducting tracts of the Pteridophyta, and particularly of the Leptosporangiate Ferns. In both the limiting surfaces are those of physiological transit : consequently in both the proportionally increased opportunity for surface-exposure will be a physiological advantage, whatever other factors may have been involved in its production.

The three critical surfaces of transit in the plant-body mentioned in the first chapter have now been considered from the point of view of Form in relation to Size. The external surface has only been lightly touched upon ; and the endodermis has only been considered incidentally, pending more exact knowledge of its permeability, and of its relation to the adjoining tissues. The chief weight of comparison has rested upon the presentation-surface of the primary woody tracts. It is believed that if the aspect of form here entertained in relation to the Size-Factor be developed, and particularly if the observer be ready to recognise homoplastic response to it in any surface of transit, morphology generally, and in particular the morphology of the conducting tracts, may enter upon a new and a more elastic phase.

CHAPTER XII

CONCLUSION

THE phenomena treated in this book all spring from that trend towards increase in size which is common in greater or less degree to all living things. We have already seen how Herbert Spencer in 1867 showed that, of the two kingdoms, plants are accumulators of material while animals are expenders. Consequently it may be expected that the Problem of Size will affect the plant-body in special degree. Their organisation gives rise to that unlimited scheme upon which the higher plants are built, with its continued embryogeny, and its geometrical ratio of increase in number of the members produced. These familiar facts point towards an acute incidence in them of the consequences of increasing size.

Of all the factors which influence Form in growing organisms there is none so immanent and inevitable as the Size-Relation. Light, temperature, water-relation, contact, and such other circumstances as affect and ultimately determine Form, may be temporary in their incidence, or fluctuating in their intensity and orientation. Even the stimulus of gravity is evanescent as the stimulated part reacts to it, though its intensity at the earth's surface is practically constant : likewise its orientation, except where organs have been displaced from the normal position. The morphoplastic effect of gravity thus appears exceptional and special rather than general in its incidence. But the effect of increasing size upon growing organisms, and particularly the changes which it brings upon the proportion of surface to bulk, is universally insistent during growth, and in the absence or insufficiency of the response its incidence becomes steeper the greater the size attained. It cannot be avoided either under conditions of Nature, or under experiment : though the size itself may be varied under changes of nutrition. When we reflect that all acquisition of nourishment and transference of material in living organisms, excepting the movement of fluid in bulk, is carried out through limiting surfaces, the physiological importance of that factor which affects the proportion of surface to bulk is evident. Of less moment physiologically than this, but governed also by the principle of similarity, is the relation of weight and mass to mechanical strength and power of resistance, upon which stability depends.

Since between a lower limit of actual size where surface tensions are dominant, and an upper limit where mechanical stability fails, all growing organisms are necessarily subject to the incidence of the size-factor, it may be anticipated that reactions of form in relation to it will probably be similar in general character, and at times even in detail, in organisms of quite distinct evolutionary origin. Analogies of change of form in relation to size may be observed between animals and plants, or between distinct types of either kingdom : or even between different parts of the individuals of either. A step then towards a just estimate of the effect of increase of size on form will be to enquire, on the basis of wide observation, how far those modifications of form which accompany enlargement in various evolutionary lines serve to meet the inevitable demands that follow from it, be these merely mechanical or intimately physiological. In the absence of direct experiment the study of such ready-made results by measurement appears to be the best means of demonstrating the incidence of the size-factor. Indeed, the field of organic nature herself presents us with a laboratory wherein she has arranged her own experiments. The acquisition from plants of such data as she supplies has been the object in view in collecting the observations and measurements detailed in the preceding chapters. So far as they demonstrate that the results accord with the demands imposed by the principle of similarity, so far will they justify the recognition of the Size-Factor as an influence on Form. Doubtless this is only one factor among many which co-operate in the determination of form : but it appears to be in its very nature the most constant and inevitable among those causal factors which may be designated " morphoplastic." Hitherto, though duly recognised and studied by Zoologists, the size-factor has not been given the place which it demands in discussions on plant-morphology.

It is true that Haberlandt in his *Physiological Plant-Anatomy* has introduced the principle of maximum exposure, and has applied it with clarifying effect to the photosynthetic and ventilating systems (Engl. Edn. 1914, pp. 66, 276, 433). But he did not apply it generally to all surfaces of transit, nor in particular to the conducting tracts. It is when the principle is applied generally, and when it is placed in relation to the law of similarity, that it attains its due place in the morphology of growing organisms. For as the size increases, if the form be unchanged, the proportion of surface to bulk constantly diminishes. Any elaboration of form tends to compensate for the contingent loss of proportion of any surface upon which transit depends. Thus as size increases, other things being equal, increasing complexity of form, if it occur, will aid physiological efficiency : indeed it may become a necessary condition.

Boycott, in a stimulating paper ' On the Size of Things, or the importance of being rather small ' (*Contr. to Med. and Biol. Research*, dedicated to Sir W. Osler, New York, 1919, pp. 226-234), has pointed out that taking statistics of species and measurements of Beetles and Moths, ' the size which fits best with the rest of the world is quite small, and not very much above the lower limit of size

found for its series.' The distribution of sizes among
fishes and mammals follows the same rule. On a general
survey ' small sorts are more advantageously placed than
their larger relations to meet the rough and tumble of
life.' On the other hand Palæontology shows that many
phyletic series have begun with those of relatively small
size, have progressed in size and complexity, and at the
climax of development have disappeared for ever.
Hence the doctrine of extinction by gigantism. In this
the Elephant, Rhinoceros, and Whale may be expected
to follow the *Dinotherium*. A parallel may be traced in
the plant kingdom. Though many of the most primitive
land-plants were quite small, and some related types still
exist, early vascular plants of large size belonging to many
distinct phyla have died out, leaving in the present world-
flora representatives of relatively small size. The difficulties inherent in large size thus appear to be cognate for
both kingdoms ; but they are not the same in detail,
though the net consequences are analogous. At the back
of all stands the mechanical limit of effective stability,
which applies equally to animals and to plants, whenever
the size is increased unduly while the material and the
scheme of construction remain the same. But in morphology the question of a mechanical limit of resistance
presents much less intimate interest than that of the proportion of bulk to those surfaces where transmission of
material is involved. As this will have to take an important place in the study of form in plants, the discussion
has been concentrated upon it.

The relation of the absorptive surface to the size of the
organism has lately been discussed from the zoological side
by Professor R. Hesse (*Ueber Grenzen des Wachsthums*,
Fischer, Jena, 1927). He brings many examples from the
lower Metazoa in support of the thesis that body-size is a
function of the absorptive surface of the gut. His drawings
to scale of three species of *Pleurogenes* demonstrate that

a size-relation exists between length of gut and length of body, but without elaboration of the form of either. The gut-surface of the largest is clearly in excess of that of the smallest, giving the impression that the gut-surface and body-size are closely related (Fig. 66). A greater interest

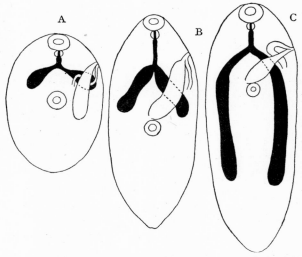

FIG. 66.—Three species of the genus *Pleurogenes*, showing their relative sizes correctly. The gut is black. A = *P. confusus* (1·3 mm. long) : B = *P. meaians* (1·5 to 2·0 mm. long) : C. = *P. claviger* (as much as 3·3 mm. in length). After Looss, from Dr. R. Hesse.

for our comparisons is presented by his drawings of ecto-parasitic Trematodes. Here the progressive increase of gut-surface is produced by divarication, which is associated with progressive increase of the body (Fig. 67). His general conclusion is that ' The size of the body is a function of the gut-surface, in other words that the development of the gut determines the limit of growth.' At the moment we need not discuss this point of causality : what is im-portant for us in the present connection is the change of form which gives an increasing area of gut-surface as the organism itself increases. In the Trematode Worms the manner of the elaboration of its contour offers an analogy with the outline of the surfaces of transit seen in the primary conducting tracts of certain plants. In both the increasing complexity of form may be held as a set-off to that contingent loss of area in proportion to bulk, which the law of similarity would entail upon the enlarging organism. This brief allusion to instances in animals, which might be greatly extended with similar results by reference to the writings of D'Arcy Thompson, Bidder, Julian Huxley, and

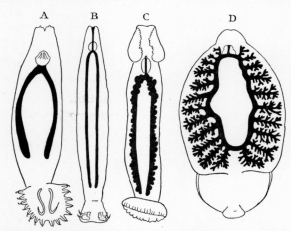

FIG. 67.—Ectoparasitic Trematodes, reduced to the same scale, the actual dimensions being stated below.
A = *Gyrodactylus elegans* (0·5 × 0·08 mm.).
B = *Amphibdella torpedinis* (3·5 × 0·45 mm.).
C = *Calceostoma elegans* (10 × 1 mm.).
D = *Epibdella hippoglossi* (24 × 13 mm.).
After Luke, Perugia and Parona, and van Benedin : from Dr. R. Hesse.

others, must suffice to suggest that a parallel exists between representatives of the two kingdoms, in respect of the relation of structure to size.

Similar analogies may be found on comparison of the chloroplasts of Algae, which are known to vary greatly both in size and form, the more complex outlines being presented by those of larger size.[1] The detailed observations of Miss Carter on Desmids provide interesting examples (*Ann. of Bot.* vol. xxxiii, 1919, pp. 215, 295 ; vol. xxxiv, 1920, pp. 265, 295). The chloroplast is a circumscribed body, its limiting surface being clearly defined from

[1] I owe the suggestion of this analogy to Prof. M. Drummond.

the surrounding cytoplasm. It is a surface of transit in relation to photosynthesis, and it may be seen to react to size independently of the limit of the protoplast, or of the cell-wall that encloses it. In fact the proportion of surface to bulk as the size of the chloroplast increases will bear a like functional importance with that of an internal physiologically active cell or tissue. In the Desmids the cells are often relatively large, with a median constriction :

FIG. 68.—Transverse sections of cells of *Closterium*, showing flanged chloroplasts, with central pyrenoid. 1 = *Cl. Dianæ* Ehrenb. : 2 = *Cl. junciaium* Ralfs : 3 = *Cl. striolatum* Ehrenb. : all are to the same scale, but reduced from Miss Carter's drawings to × 510, for purposes of comparison with Figs. 69 and 70. After Miss N. Carter.

usually there is one chloroplast in each half-cell, but sometimes more than one. Where the size is considerable the chloroplast is often found to be flanged, ridges running longitudinally, and projecting outwards. Sometimes the ridges remain separate, but often they are connected laterally to form an irregular network. The appearance of the chloroplast in transverse section is stellate, as is seen in Fig. 68. The ridges though variable in number are fairly constant for the species. Their number shows a relation to size. This relation is suggested by the adjoining table, which is based upon drawings of five species of *Closterium* by Miss Carter (*Ann. of Bot.* xxxiii, Pl. XIV, XV).

TABLE XXV

Name and Reference to Miss Carter's Figures.	Mean Diameter in mm. (× 810).	Number of Flanges.	Ratio of Diameter to Number of Flanges.
Cl. Dianæ (Fig. 37) - -	10	6	1·6
Cl. juncidium (Fig. 48) -	12	7	1·7
Cl. angustatum (Fig. 36) -	20	10	2·0
Cl. striolatum (Fig. 42) -	23	13	1·8
Cl. Lunula (Fig. 4) - -	53	15	3·5

The last column gives the ratio of the diameter of the chloroplast (× 810) to the number of its flanges. A fair level of uniformity appears in the lower terms of the series, though the ratio rises notably in the last, which is an out-size. This has its interest for comparison with the vascular tracts in stems and roots. (Compare Tables IV, p. 30, XXII, p. 172.)

The elaboration of form of the chloroplasts of Desmids is, however, carried much further in extreme cases than the mere presence of flanges, giving stellation in transverse

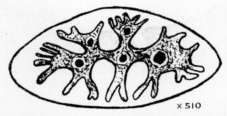

FIG. 69.—Transverse sections of cells of *Micrasterias*, showing progressive elaboration of the chloroplasts with increasing size. The smaller is *M. pinnatifida* (Kütz) Ralfs : the larger *M. oscitans* Ralfs. The scale is the same as in Figs. 68 and 70. After Miss N. Carter.

section. The flanges may themselves branch freely when the size of the cell is greater. This is well shown in *Micrasterias*, by comparing the smaller *M. pinnatifida* and its 8-flanged chloroplast with the larger *M. oscitans*, where the flanges number over 20 (Fig. 69). Moreover, numerous peg-like processes may project radially outwards from the chloroplasts, as in the very large cells of *Cosmarium Askenasyi* (Fig. 70). Other details of elaboration also appear where the size is great, combined as in *Cosmarium* with disintegration of the chloroplasts, and even with decentralisation so as to leave a clear central space in the cell, comparable in position with a pith.

In the Zygnemeæ a progression of increasing complexity with size is indicated by contrasting the simple median plate-like chloroplast of *Mougeotia* with the spiral chloroplasts of *Spirogyra,* one or more in each cell. The latter are frilled at their margins in the larger species, as are also the flanges in the large cells of *Closterium.* In *Mougeotia* the British species range from 3µ to 35µ in diameter : those of *Spirogyra* range from 10µ to 150µ, while *Zygnema* with its stellate chloroplasts appears to take a middle position in point of size. All these facts of elaboration go with

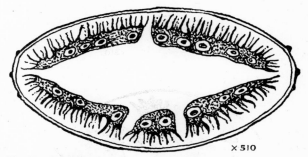

× 510

FIG. 70.—Transverse section of cell of *Cosmarium Askenasyi* Schmidle. Showing numerous chloroplasts surrounding a central space, and bearing peg-like processes directed outwards. After Miss N. Carter. The scale is the same as in Figs. 68, 69.

increasing dimensions. The changes in form of the chloroplasts are such as will tend to level up the contingent loss of proportion of surface to bulk consequent on enlargement, and they may be quite independent of change in the outline of the whole cell. This appears in all of the drawings quoted above. But it is not always so : for instance in the genus *Micrasterias* involutions of outline of the large flattened cell coincide with those of the chloroplast within (Fig. 71). Elaboration in form of the chloroplasts appears also in the enlarging cells of other Algae. For instance in *Œdogonium* the single chloroplast may be slit longitudinally into rods, which are connected here and there laterally, so as to form a continuous but highly interrupted cylinder (Fig. 72, 1). Similarly in

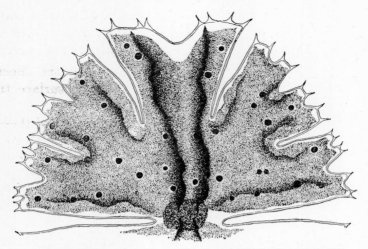

FIG. 71.—Half of a cell of *Micrasterias apiculata* (Ehrenb.) Menegh. (× 510).
The scale is the same as that in Figs. 68-70. Here the outline of the very large
cell corresponds roughly to that of the chloroplast. After Miss N. Carter.

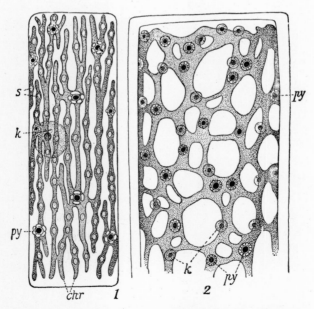

FIG. 72.—1 = The chromatophore of an *Œdogonium*-cell: 2, that of *Cladophora arcta*. *k* = nucleus : *py* = pyrenoid. After Schmitz : from Oltmanns.

Cladophora the chloroplast is a cylindrical network, with meshes of irregular shape and size (Fig. 72, 2). All of these chloroplasts offer analogies of form with the elaborated stelar tracts in Leptosporangiate Ferns : while the effect in both is the maintenance of the ratio of surface to bulk.

In strong contrast to the elaborate chloroplasts of these Algae stand those of the Ulvaceæ, Siphoneæ, and Characeæ, and of the higher plants generally. Here the individual chloroplast remains small, and the form is simple. The proportion of surface to bulk is high, being maintained by the flattened discoid form, and by the simple fact that the growing chloroplast divides as soon as it attains a small average size. The advantage which this method possesses is shown by its general adoption in land-living plants : they thus maintain a high surface of exposure of the photosynthetic organ, the chloroplast. The principle is the same as that which rules in the disintegration of the conducting tracts in advanced Leptosporangiate Ferns, though the detail is quite different.

In Chapter XI, p. 190, the relation of the outline of the endodermis to the sculpturing of the xylem has been discussed, and it was seen that though frequently there is no near relation between them where the dimensions are small, where the size is greater the endodermis tends to follow the contours of the xylem. This appears particularly in the protosteles of certain large Coenopterid Ferns (Fig. 21), and in the large roots of Aroids and Palms (Figs. 59-61). A like relation appears also between the outline of the cell in the Desmids and that of the chloroplast. Where the size is small the chloroplast may be elaborately moulded, though the contour of the cell is smooth (Figs. 68, 69). This is seen even in the relatively large cylindrical cells of *Spirogyra* or *Cladophora* (Fig. 72). But in contrast to this stand the large cells of certain Desmids, and a prominent example is seen in such an out-size as *Micrasterias apiculata*

(Fig. 71). In either case it appears that the surfaces in question present separate and distinct problems, though both are subject to the common impress of a size-relation. It cannot be rightly assumed that, because they sometimes react alike the problem is the same for each. It must remain for physiologists to consider such facts in relation to function. The morphologist sees in the collective presentation-surface of tracheal tissue and of endodermis two quite distinct things : and similarly the presentation-surface of the chloroplast and the cell-outline are essentially distinct. He notes that in certain cases, particularly where the dimensions are relatively great, they react alike : where relatively small they do not. It will lie with the physiologist to explain such happenings, probably in terms of permeability. But whatever the interpretation, the fact remains that the elaboration of form of either has the effect of tending to maintain the presentation-surface.

Comparison in point of the ratio of diameter to the number of flanges, in respect of the chloroplasts of *Closterium* on the one hand, and of the primary conducting tracts of Pteridophytes on the other, brings very striking results. If the tables showing the ratio of diameter to number of flanges in the radial steles of *Psilotum* (p. 18), or of *Lycopodium* (p. 30), or of the roots of *Danæa* (p. 166), or of *Colocasia* (p. 172) be compared with that for the chloroplasts of *Closterium* (p. 214), approximately a like constancy of ratio appears in each, but with a tendency to rise as outsizes are approached. Though the actual dimensions are very different, there is a like size-relation in the stellation of them all ; but the parts compared are essentially diverse.

The polyphyletic origin of such various instances of modification of form in relation to increasing size, and the tendency at the back of them all to maintain that presentation-surface which physiologists hold as important ; the similarity of the methods that produce this result in organisms that are not akin, and in parts that are of distinct category ; and the fact that the tissues or other units which present these similarities of form are often internal in the plant-body : all provide material for a view of Form somewhat detached from the old descriptive morphology of tissues. The new aspect is related to conditions not hitherto sufficiently recognised for them. The facts suggest some power of adjustment, individual or racial, or both, tending to maintain a due proportion of the surfaces of transit to the bulk contained by them. The expression the ' Size-Factor ' has been used to designate such power in the title and in the text of this book ; and the demand may reasonably be made that it should be defined. The difficulty will be to define what is known as yet only by its results. For example, we see in the mature stele of a root that such or such a form has been attained, so many rays or protoxylems in the stellate stele of such or such a size : so many in a larger one. We pursue the question towards the apical meristem, to the point where the rays are first recognisable ; and we find that immediately below the growing point their complex outline is already visible. But these tissues at their first inception as conducting tissues are not functional as such, and are much smaller than they are in the matured root, which will prospectively develop to such or such a size. We do not know what the determining influence is which brings them into being, or how it is made effective. Yet the matured structure constantly tends to meet the demand, according to the principle of similarity. Are we then to deny the existence of a determining cause, because we cannot define it ? Surely it will be better to retain provisionally a conception of compliance to such demands. We may, however, locate the first visible signs of such compliance in the region immediately below the extreme tip. We may even give it a colourless name, such as the ' *Size-Factor,*' and suggest that its action is *morphoplastic* : that is, that it induces by change such mature form as shall tend to maintain a due proportion of surface to bulk.   (See Preface.)

We know further that the outline and relations of the conducting tracts are susceptible of change according to the conditions, *as the individual part increases or diminishes.* Flaskämper has found that the pith of an individual root may come and go according to nutrition. · Further, he showed that in starved roots of *Vicia Faba* there may not only be a reduction in the number of tracheids, but even in the rays of the xylem.   These in a given case fell from six to five, and even to four (*Flora*, Bd. ci, p. 207).   Such structural consequences of starvation were reversed in the distal region when the conditions allowed of normal nutrition.   This agrees with the starvation results recorded by Mettenius for the stem of *Angiopteris*, in which a normal structure below, with 60 meristeles in the transverse section, contracted upward to 35 meristeles, owing to their less high segregation following on defective culture (see *Ferns*, vol. ii, p. 102, Fig. 307).   Again, in a plant of *Deparia Moorei*, similarly starved, J. McL. Thompson showed how the normal perforated dictyostele of the stem contracted upwards, with a near approach to simple solenostely.   The diameter of the normal dictyostele was about 2·35 mm., that of the starved solenostele 1·16 mm. (*Trans. R. S. Edin.* vol. l, p. 840).   The interest presented by results such as these does not lie only in the changed size-relation of the adult, whether shoot or root, but in the fact that the vascular tracts must have been laid down in the apical region of either, long before the adult size had been reached.   There seems to have been at the tip some anticipatory, or ' proleptic ' sensitiveness to the incidence of similarity.   It is this which would determine a stelar structure suitable to the size ultimately to be attained.   In the above instances this anticipation is seen to be shared alike by roots and axes, and it exists independently of appendages.

The apical cone from this point of view is as wonderful a thing as the initial embryo itself, which may indeed be held to delegate its powers to the apices of the several parts. Like other embryological features the primary vascular tracts originate on a smaller scale than they may finally attain. What is remarkable about this is that their number as well as their final detail is related as we have seen to size, in accordance with dimensions not yet existent. Moreover the facts of mature structure show that the relation is in some degree *individually* adjustable at the apex according to what those dimensions will eventually be. This is particularly clear in roots where there are no appendages.

In the shoot a parallel may be seen in the number of leaves in a whorl, which is liable sometimes to vary in the individual plant in relation to the strength of the shoot which bears them, giving that meristic variation which is seen both in vegetative and in floral buds. Thus, whether in the production of external appendages or of the internal structure of the conducting system, the determination of the number of units lies with the apical cone. Professor Von Goebel, when discussing the relation of the leaf-arrangement in radial shoots to the outer world, writes as follows (*Organographie*, III Aufl., Teil I, pp. 299, 300) : ' At the present time variety of position cannot be regarded as the consequence of adaptation. This much is proved, so far as we can see : that the question relates to conditions of growth and symmetry which arise in the growing point : also that all theories as to leaf-position that allotted—so to speak—a passive rôle to the growing point were mistaken, however acute the reasoning that was brought to bear thereon.' This is Von Goebel's final summing up for external parts. A like reference of the origin and disposition of the internal conducting tracts to the growing point appears to be equally justified.

That anticipatory power of adjustment to ultimate size which thus appears in the initiation of internal tissue tracts appears to be independent of the direct action of external influences. It harmonises readily with the 'holistic' views of General Smuts. Notwithstanding the continued embryogeny of the plant, the structural well-being of the shoot or root as a whole is continuously determined by the activity of the apical meristem, in the same way as is the primary differentiation and establishment of parts in the embryo itself. In point of fact the apical cone may be held to act as a perennial sector of the original embryo, in so far as it retains its power of initiation.

It will be realised from the detailed facts and the conclusions which have been advanced in this volume that there will have to be some revision of the morphology of the conducting system. That though the influence of branching or of the insertion of appendages may explain many structural facts, yet this does not suffice for all. Apart from such disturbing influences as these, the conducting tracts react independently to other factors : among them the Size-Factor is certainly one. This appears to follow necessarily from the numerous instances quoted in this book, which have been taken from the primary conducting system, and chiefly in relation to the collective surface of transit where tracheal elements face upon living cells. But if the reasoning applied to it is sound, like questions may arise as to the size-relation of any other surface of transit : in particular, to the endodermis, and to the limiting surface by which any organism faces its environment. In the study of these, and especially in the behaviour of the endodermis in relation to the size-factor, complicated questions of permeability will arise, which fall in the first instance rather within the sphere of the physiologist than of the morphologist. But from the point of view of Form, so far as the transit of material is proportional to the area exposed, the effect of increasing Size will necessarily be to demand changes in contour, whether of endodermis or of the external limiting surface of the shoot or part, of the same nature as those affecting the tracheal surfaces.

It is the success of the higher land plants in evading the incidence of the size-factor by adaptive structure, which has disguised the demands from which their continued growth appears to be inseparable. Those who think primarily or perhaps exclusively in terms of the highest organisation are in danger of forgetting that a very large section of the Vegetable Kingdom was evolved with simpler structure. It should be realised that three leading morphological features have contributed very greatly to the success of any large tree, or in less degree of any ordinary herbaceous Dicotyledon : viz. continued embryogeny, internal ventilation, and cambial activity. The first of these originated early in evolution ; but the other two were relatively late innovations, from the point of view of the plant-kingdom at large, and the Thallophytes (excepting some Brown Algae) and Bryophyta, have developed without them. These three features have in combination satisfied the demands of increasing size in advanced types of vegetation. The two last provide an automatically increasing surface of exposure respectively of the tracheal elements to living cells, and of internal cells to the atmosphere, so as to secure interchange. Meanwhile that critical feature of primary vascular structure, the endodermis, is normally obliterated as a consequence of secondary growth in such plants as possess it. Thus provided and emancipated, the higher Seed-Plant can progress till the limit of mechanical resistance is reached. But it is not by the study of such advanced types as these, which have successfully met the most pressing difficulties of increasing size, that the problem of the size-relation can best be studied. It is by comparison of those earlier forms which, owing to their primitive structure, fall more directly under its sway. The Algae and the Bryophytes, in which internal ventilation and cambial increase are virtually absent, together with the more primitive Pteridophytes, provide a field that yields more suggestive material for the solution of the evolutionary Problem of Size than do all the higher Seed-Plants put together. Particularly is this so in respect of the conducting tracts of the most primitive land plants, with their imperfectly vitalised wood. That is the reason why this study of the Size-Factor in plant-morphology has been based upon the primary conducting system as it is seen in them.

Nevertheless the conducting tracts provide only a single phase of the morphological problem of size in plants, while its incidence is of necessity quite general. Sooner or later a new morphology of all tissues will have to be developed, somewhat of the nature of an internal organo-graphy, and complementary to the organography of external form. It will have as its end the causal interpretation of the form assumed by the several tissue-tracts. Those who follow this line of enquiry, will not be content with a mere formal comparison, as it exists at present : they will attempt to interpret that form throughout Descent in terms of all the factors that influence development, whether external or internal. Amongst these the Size-Factor, and its relation to the proportion and behaviour of the surfaces of transit will take a leading place.

P

INDEX OF TABLES

INDEX

PRINTED IN GREAT BRITAIN BY ROBERT MACLEHOSE AND CO. LTD.
THE UNIVERSITY PRESS, GLASGOW.